Discovering Geometry

Teacher's Resource Book

KEY CURRICULUM PRESS
Innovators in Mathematics Education

Editor	Sarah Block
Chief Copy Editor	Greer Lleuad
Editorial Assistant	James A. Browne
Production Editor	Jason Luz
Production Manager	Luis Shein
Production Coordinator	Susan Parini
Art and Layout	Kristen Garneau, Kirk Mills, Ann Rothenbuhler

Contributors and Additional Editorial Development

Masha Albrecht, Dan Bennett, Sheldon G. Berman, Ralph Bothe, Sharon Grand, Judy Hicks, Darlene Pugh, Eberhard Scheiffele, Michael Serra, Carolyn Sessions, Luis Shein

Publisher

Steven Rasmussen

Editorial Director

John Bergez

The Geometer's Sketchpad® Demonstrations Disks

Key Curriculum Press guarantees that the disks that accompany this book are free of defects in materials and workmanship. A defective disk will be replaced free of charge if returned within 90 days of the purchase date. After 90 days there is a $10 replacement fee.

Limited Reproduction Permission

Key Curriculum Press
P.O. Box 2304
Berkeley CA 94702
(510) 548-2304
editorial@keypress.com
http://www.keypress.com

Printed in the United States of America   10 9 8 7 6 5 4 3 2   01 00 99 98 97   ISBN 1-55953-202-5

Contents

Annotated Bibliography and Lists of Geometry Resources

Discovering Geometry
Teacher's Support Materials

Teacher's Guide and Answer Key
- Overview and philosophy
- Course outlines
- Cooperative learning suggestions
- Assessment suggestions
- Lesson guides
- Answers for exercises
- Answers for puzzles
- Answers for projects
- Answers for Cooperative Problem-Solving lessons
- Answers for Take Another Look activities
- Lists of conjectures, postulates, and theorems
- Glossary

Teacher's Resource Book
- Transparency and worksheet masters
- Extra practice worksheets
- Extra projects
- Activity masters for Geometer's Sketchpad® demonstrations
- Bibliography of geometry resources
- Geometer's Sketchpad demonstrations on disks for Windows® and Macintosh® computers

Quizzes, Tests, and Exams
- At least four quizzes per chapter
- Construction review quizzes
- Coordinate geometry quizzes
- Form A and Form B chapter tests with student answer sheets
- Form A and Form B exams (midyear and final) for five different course plans with student answer sheets
- Answers to quizzes, tests, and exams
- CD-ROM with quizzes, tests, and exams formatted for Microsoft Word for Windows and Macintosh computers

Constructive Assessment in Mathematics
Practical Steps for Classroom Teachers
by David Clarke
- Guide to implementing assessment strategies, including observational assessment, student-constructed tests, group assessment, student self-assessment, student journals, and portfolios
- Tips for recording, interpreting, and communicating assessment information
- Annotated bibliography of assessment resources

Discovering Geometry with The Geometer's Sketchpad
- Blackline masters for *Discovering Geometry* lessons adapted for use with The Geometer's Sketchpad, a Dynamic Geometry™ software tool separately available from Key Curriculum Press
- Disks for Windows and Macintosh computers with Geometer's Sketchpad sketches and scripts for the lessons in this volume

Suggested Supplemental Resources

The Geometer's Sketchpad
- Dynamic geometry software for Windows and Macintosh

Patty Paper Geometry, by Michael Serra
- Additional discovery lessons with patty papers
- Additional practice exercises for the basic geometry properties discovered in *Discovering Geometry*

Mathercise, by Michael Serra
- A set of 50 blackline masters to use as class warm-up exercises

Lénárt Sphere™ Construction Materials
- A manipulative kit containing spheres; the spherical equivalents of a compass, a straightedge, a protractor, and a ruler; and other materials for investigating spherical geometry
- Non-Euclidean Adventures on the Lénárt Sphere: a book of over 40 blackline master spherical geometry activities

Overview of Teacher's Resource Book

The *Discovering Geometry Teacher's Resource Book* is a versatile resource designed to supplement the lessons, investigations, projects, activities, and exercises in the student text. The six sections of the *Teacher's Resource Book* contain a guide to supplementary resources, transparency and worksheet masters, extra practice worksheets, additional geometry projects, Geometer's Sketchpad demonstration activity masters and disks, and an annotated bibliography and annotated lists of geometry resources. Each section begins with an introductory page that recommends how and when to use the materials. We hope this resource book will provide you with years of interesting and useful ideas to use in your *Discovering Geometry* classroom.

Supplementary Resource Guide
Tables listing resources available for the lessons in the student text. The resources include those contained in this book, in *Discovering Geometry Quizzes, Tests, and Exams,* in *Discovering Geometry with The Geometer's Sketchpad,* and in *Non-Euclidean Adventures on the Lénárt Sphere.*

Transparency and Worksheet Masters
Blackline masters to assist you in your presentations to the class. The masters contain illustrations, demonstrations, and selected exercises from the student text.

Extra Practice Worksheets
Supplemental exercises for some of the curriculum's core lessons. The exercises can be used to assist students who have difficulty with a particular concept, to give as extra credit material, or both.

Additional Geometry Projects
Projects that supplement those featured in the student text. Many of these projects are among the *Discovering Geometry* field testers' favorites. They include geometry review games, art projects, a topology project, and a map-coloring project.

Geometer's Sketchpad Demonstrations
Activities designed to introduce you to The Geometer's Sketchpad. No prior Sketchpad experience is necessary. Each computer activity includes a worksheet master. The disks in the back of this book provide the demonstration version of Sketchpad to use on computers running Microsoft® Windows® (version 3.1 or later) and on Macintosh® computers. You do not need the full-featured program to use these demonstrations.

Annotated Bibliography and Lists of Geometry Resources
A comprehensive list of geometry resources that includes books, posters, visuals, software, manipulatives, puzzles, toys, and videos—all of which you can use to stimulate and support the study of high school geometry. The materials on the lists can easily be adapted for use with students at all levels of mathematical understanding.

Supplementary Resource Guide

The *Discovering Geometry* supplementary resources listed in the following tables were created to be appropriate for specific lessons. The tables are set up so that you can easily identify the resources available for a particular lesson. The table on the last pages of this section will assist you in identifying which of this book's additional geometry projects are appropriate to use with a particular chapter or lesson—many of these projects can be used with several different chapters. Resources available for every lesson, such as the lesson guides in the *Teacher's Guide and Answer Key,* are not identified in the tables.

The transparency and worksheet masters (T/W), extra practice worksheets, and Geometer's Sketchpad demonstrations can all be found in this book. The remaining resources can be found in other *Discovering Geometry* teacher's support materials: the quizzes can be found in *Quizzes, Tests, and Exams* (QTE), the Sketchpad activities can be found in *Discovering Geometry with The Geometer's Sketchpad* (DG w/GSP). The Lénárt Sphere adventures can be found in a separate publication available from Key Curriculum Press, *Non-Euclidean Adventures on the Lénárt Sphere*— note that the adventures are listed in the order in which they are most relevant to the lesson, not in numerical order.

Refer to the lesson guides in the *Teacher's Guide and Answer Key* for more information on resources.

	TRB			QTE	DG w/GSP	Lénárt Sphere
Lesson	T/W exercises/ investigations	Extra practice worksheet	Sketchpad demos	Quizzes	Activities	Adventures
Chapter 0: Geometric Art						
0.1						
0.2	√				√	
0.3					√	
0.4					√	
0.5						
0.6	√					
0.7					√	
0.8	√				√	
0.9						
Chapter 1: Inductive Reasoning						
1.1						
1.2		√				
1.3	√			√		

Lesson	TRB			QTE	DG w/GSP	Lénárt Sphere
	T/W exercises/ investigations	Extra practice worksheet	Sketchpad demos	Quizzes	Activities	Adventures
Chapter 1 (cont.)						
1.4	√	√		√		
1.5	√	√				
1.6	√			√		
1.7	√					
Chapter 2: Introducing Geometry						
2.1	√					0.1, 1.1, 1.2
2.2	√					1.5
2.3	√			√		1.3, 3.1
2.4						2.1, 2.2, 2.3
2.5				√		3.1
2.6					√	3.1, 3.2, 3.3
2.7	√		√	√	√	6.1
2.8	√					
2.9	√			√		
2.10	√	√				
Chapter 3: Using the Tools of Geometry						
3.1						1.3, 1.5
3.2	√			√	√	
3.3	√				√	
3.4				√	√	
3.5						2.1
3.6				√		
3.7	√		√		√	10.3, 10.4, 10.5
3.8	√		√	√	√	10.5
3.9		√				

Lesson	TRB			QTE	DG w/GSP	Lénárt Sphere
	T/W exercises/ investigations	Extra practice worksheet	Sketchpad demos	Quizzes	Activities	Adventures

Chapter 4: Line and Angle Properties

Lesson	T/W exercises/investigations	Extra practice worksheet	Sketchpad demos	Quizzes	Activities	Adventures
4.1	√				√	2.2
4.2	√			√	√	2.1
4.3	√				√	7.2
4.4		√		√	√	
4.5		√	√	√	√	
4.6		√		√		
4.7						
4.8	√					

Chapter 5: Triangle Properties

Lesson	T/W exercises/investigations	Extra practice worksheet	Sketchpad demos	Quizzes	Activities	Adventures
5.1	√		√		√	3.4, 3.2, 3.3, 3.5
5.2	√			√	√	3.1
5.3		√		√	√	
5.4	√	√		√	√	4.3, 3.5
5.5	√	√		√	√	4.3, 3.5
5.6	√			√		
5.7	√				√	
5.8	√					

Chapter 6: Polygon Properties

Lesson	T/W exercises/investigations	Extra practice worksheet	Sketchpad demos	Quizzes	Activities	Adventures
6.1	√			√	√	3.4
6.2			√	√	√	
6.3	√			√	√	
6.4	√	√			√	
6.5	√				√	
6.6	√			√	√	6.1
6.7	√					

Lesson	TRB T/W exercises/ investigations	TRB Extra practice worksheet	TRB Sketchpad demos	QTE Quizzes	DG w/GSP Activities	Lénárt Sphere Adventures
Chapter 7: Circles						
7.1	√				√	5.1
7.2	√				√	5.1
7.3				√	√	5.1
7.4	√	√		√	√	8.1
7.5	√	√	√		√	5.3
7.6				√		
7.7		√		√		1.3
7.8	√					
Chapter 8: Transformations and Tessellations						
8.1	√				√	
8.2	√		√	√	√	
8.3	√			√	√	
8.4	√			√		9.1–9.5, 3.1
8.5	√					9.1–9.5
8.6	√		√		√	9.1–9.5
8.7	√		√		√	9.1–9.5
8.8	√		√			9.1–9.5
8.9	√					
Chapter 9: Area						
9.1	√	√		√	√	6.1, 6.2
9.2	√	√	√	√	√	6.2
9.3	√	√				6.2
9.4				√	√	6.1
9.5		√			√	6.3
9.6	√					6.3
9.7	√	√		√		
9.8		√				
9.9	√					

Lesson	TRB T/W exercises/ investigations	TRB Extra practice worksheet	TRB Sketchpad demos	QTE Quizzes	DG w/GSP Activities	Lénárt Sphere Adventures
Chapter 10: Pythagorean Theorem						
10.1	√	√	√		√	3.5
10.2		√			√	3.5
10.3		√		√		
10.4	√	√			√	3.5
10.5		√			√	8.1
10.6	√			√		
10.7	√	√		√	√	
10.8	√					
10.9	√			√		
10.10						
Chapter 11: Volume						
11.1	√					
11.2	√					9.4, 9.5
11.3	√	√		√		
11.4		√		√		
11.5		√				
11.6				√		
11.7						
11.8		√				6.2, 6.1
11.9				√		
11.10		√				
Chapter 12: Similarity						
12.1		√				
12.2	√	√		√	√	4.1, 6.1
12.3					√	4.2
12.4	√	√		√	√	
12.5		√			√	4.1
12.6		√	√	√	√	
12.7		√		√	√	
12.8						

Lesson	TRB			QTE	DG w/GSP	Lénárt Sphere
	T/W exercises/ investigations	Extra practice worksheet	Sketchpad demos	Quizzes	Activities	Adventures
Chapter 13: Trigonometry						
13.1		√		√	√	
13.2		√		√		
13.3				√	√	
13.4						
13.5		√		√		
13.6	√					
Chapter 14: Deductive Reasoning						
14.1						
14.2						
14.3		√		√		
14.4		√		√		
14.5		√		√		
14.6		√		√		
14.7	√			√		
14.8	√					
14.9	√			√		
14.10						
Chapter 15: Geometric Proof						
15.1	√					
15.2	√		√	√	√	
15.3	√			√		
15.4	√			√		
15.5						
15.6						
15.7				√		
15.8						

Lesson	TRB			QTE	DG w/GSP	Lénárt Sphere
	T/W exercises/ investigations	Extra practice worksheet	Sketchpad demos	Quizzes	Activities	Adventures
Chapter 16: Sequences of Proof						
16.1						
16.2				√		
16.3				√		
16.4						
16.5						
16.6				√		
16.7			√	√	√	
16.8						

Additional Geometry Projects

Chapters	GI*	0	1	2	3	4	5	6	7	8	9	10	11	12	13	14	15	16
Block Lettering in Perspective	√	√																
Perspective View of a Tiled Floor	√	√																
Spacing Fenceposts in Perspective	√	√																
Beehive Geometry			√															
Geopardy	√			√														
Stained Glass	√	√			√					√								
Map Coloring	√																	
Occupational Speaker	√																	
Matho	√							√										
Folding Paper Circles									√									
Symmetry in Snowflakes	√									√								
Tessellation T-shirts	√	√								√								
Building a Home											√							
Finding Another Proof of the Pythagorean Theorem												√				√	√	√
Packing Efficiency and Displacement													√					
Similarity in Grow Creatures														√				
Grow Creatures Growth Patterns														√				
The Geometry of Baseball								√							√			
A Möbius Strip: The Surface with a Twist	√																	
Writing a Logic Puzzle																√		
Proof by Mathematical Induction																	√	√

*GI: general interest

Discovering Geometry Teacher's Resource Book

Introduction to the Transparency and Worksheet Masters

The transparency and worksheet blackline masters are designed for you to use in your classroom presentations and discussions. The masters contain selected investigations and exercises, including those with illustrations and figures that are difficult or take time to draw. A list of all the masters is included in the Supplementary Resource Guide tables at the beginning of this book.

Each master is identified in its upper right-hand corner as a transparency master (T), a worksheet master (W), or a transparency/worksheet master (T/W). Transparency masters contain material from the student text, enlarged so that it can easily be seen when displayed on an overhead projector. Worksheet masters are designed as aids to be given to students when they need help performing investigations, working on special projects, or completing exercises. Transparency/worksheet masters can be used for either or both purposes.

The first two masters contain a coarse grid and a fine grid that can be reproduced for investigations that require graph paper. The ruler and protractor masters can be used to make rulers (English and metric) and protractors for yourself and your students. Use a copy machine to copy the master onto acetate, cut out the tools, and distribute them to your students. (Students can keep their ruler and protractor tucked in their books—they'll never forget to bring them to class.)

Coarse Grid Paper

T/W

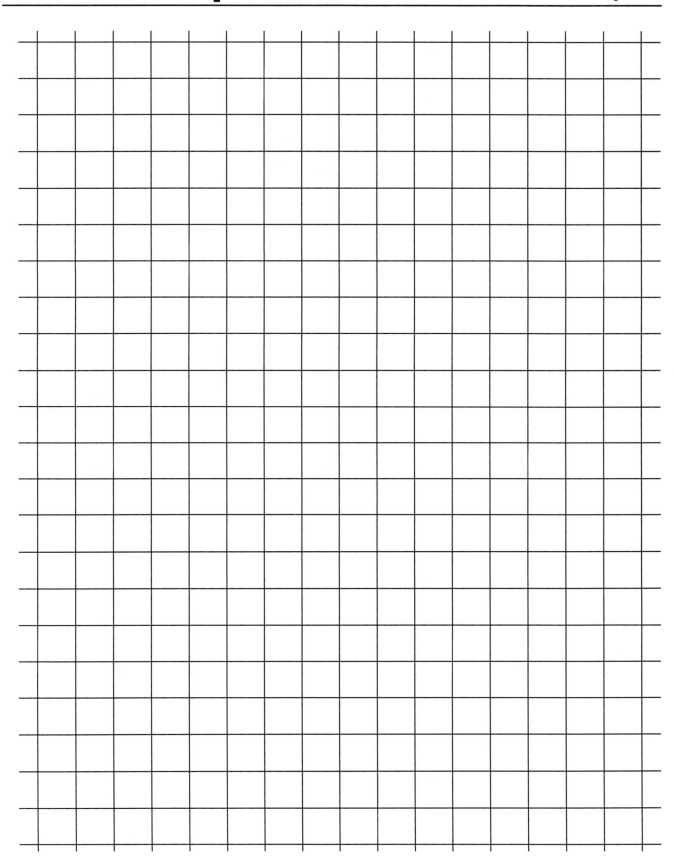

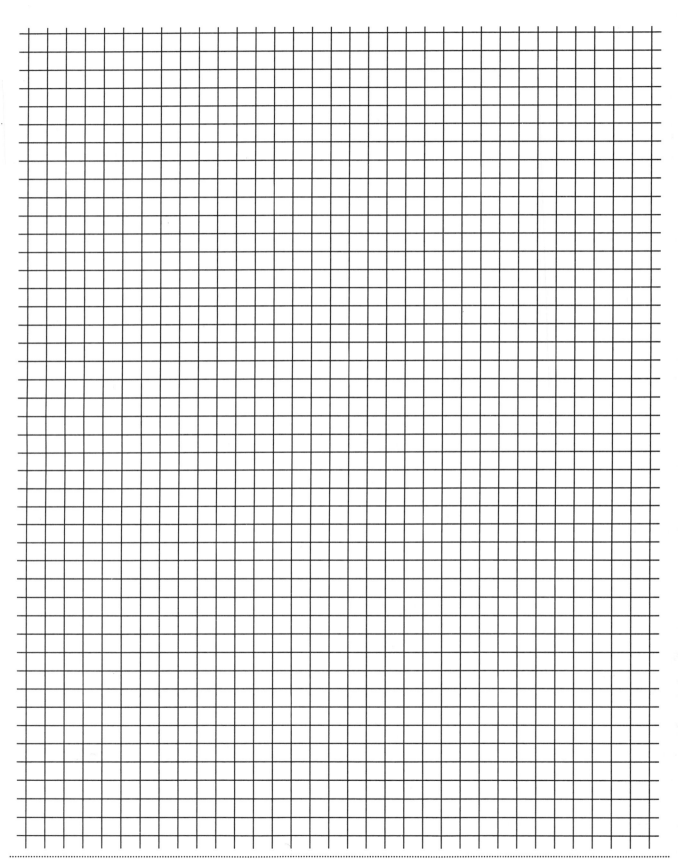

Metric and English Rulers

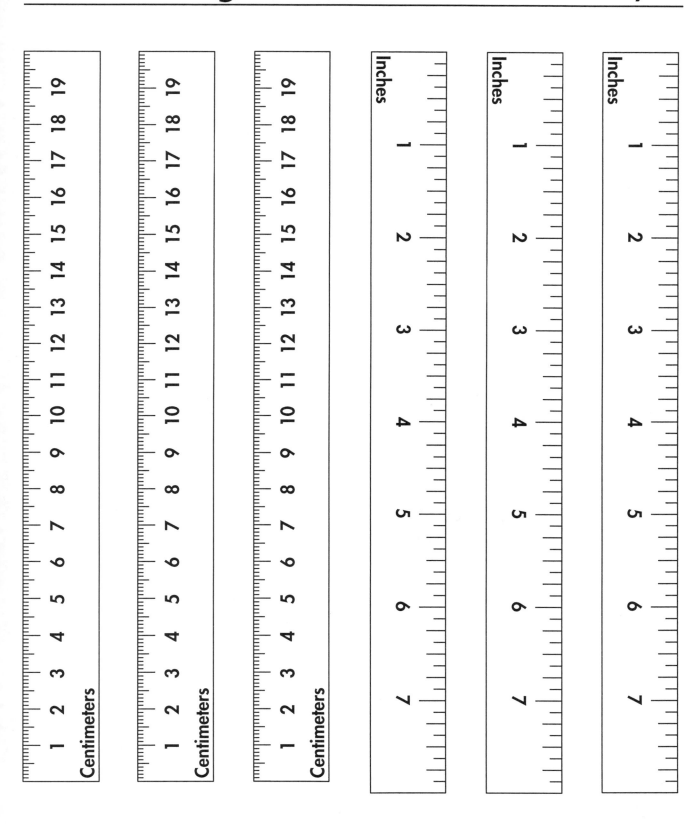

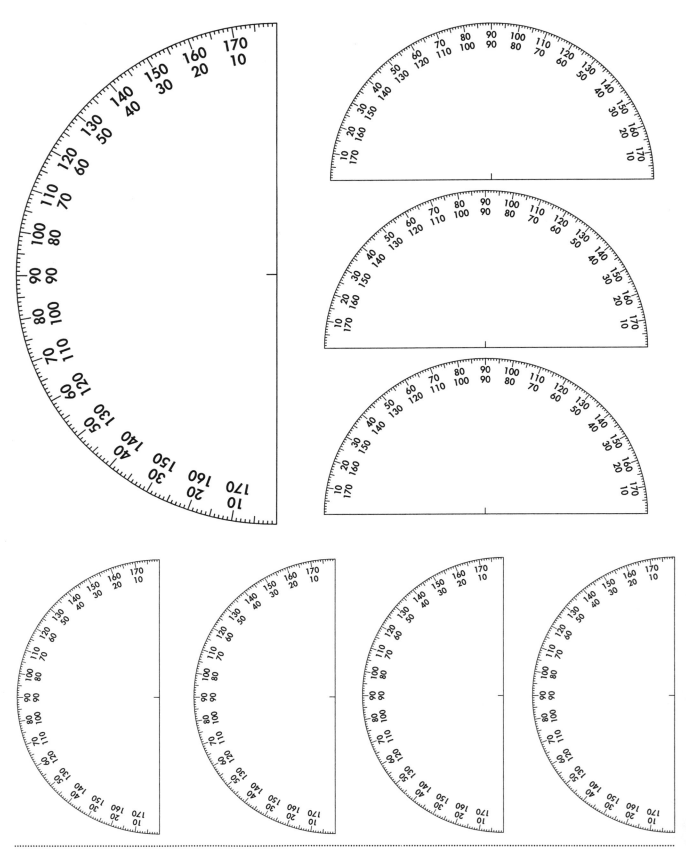

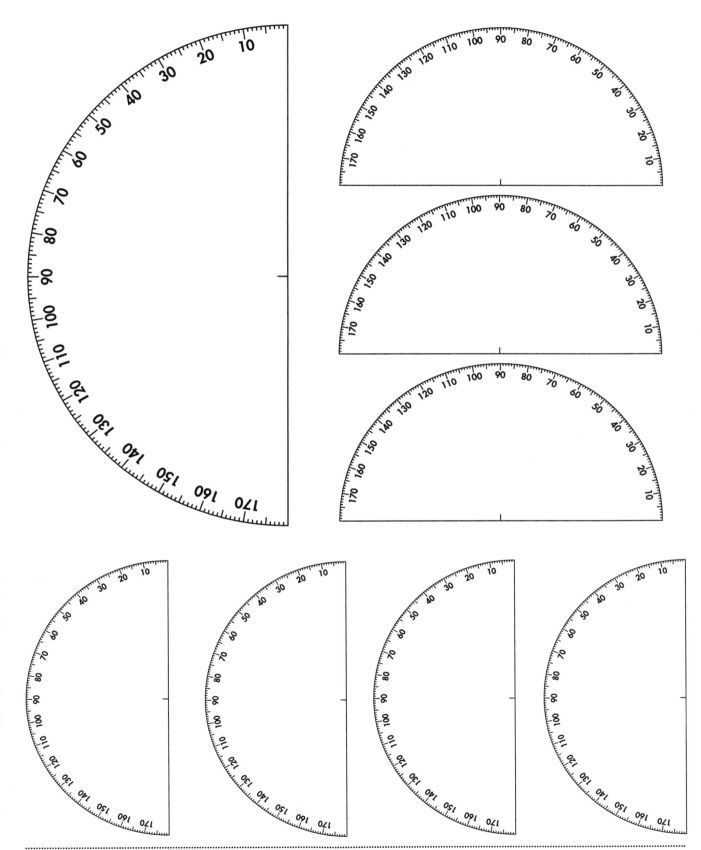

Line Designs

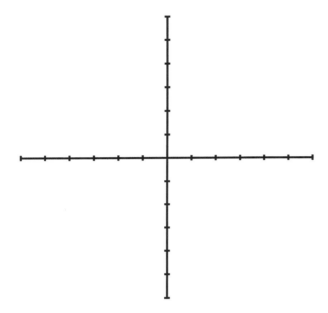

Step 1

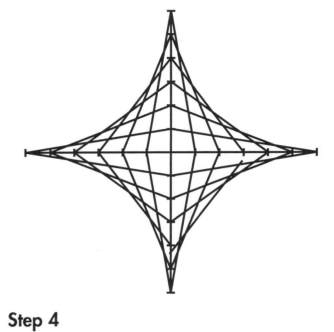

Step 4

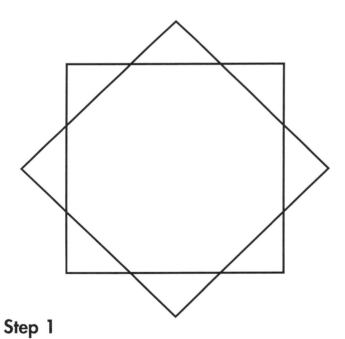

Step 1

Step 4

Exercise 4.

Borromean Rings

Exercises 1 and 5.

1.

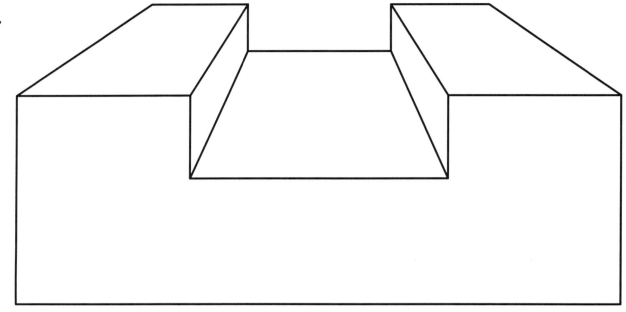

5.

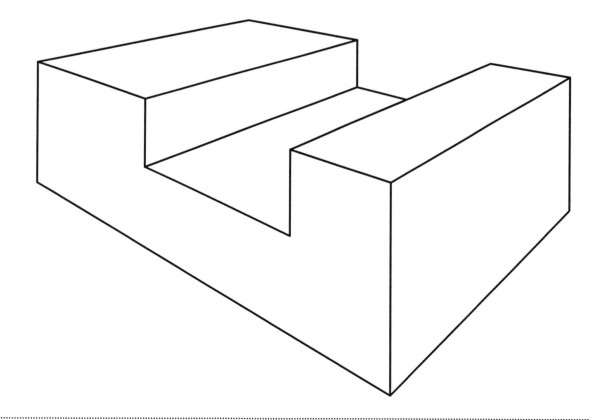

Exercises 11–14.

11.

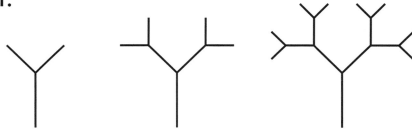

12.

13.

14.

Exercises 15–19.

15.

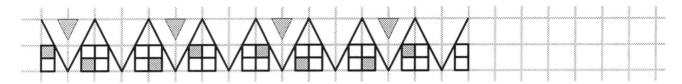

16.

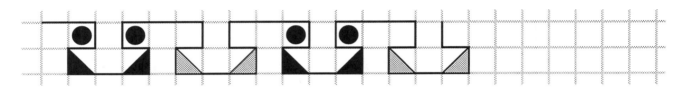

17.

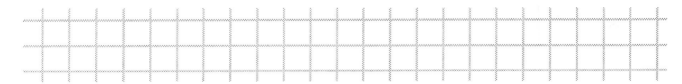

18. African woven basket design

19. Painted rafter, Maori (New Zealand)

Lesson 1.4/Page 54 **T/W**

Exercises 5 and 6.

5.

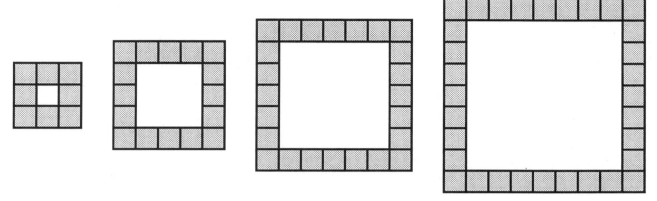

Squares in a square donut

Donut	1	2	3	4	5	6	...	n	...	200
Number of squares	8	16					...		...	

6.

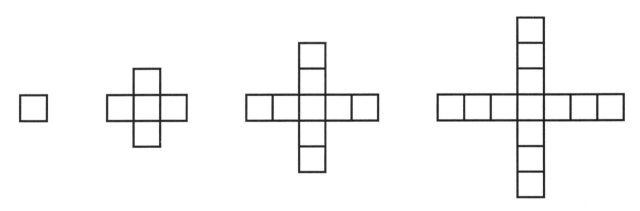

Squares in a cross array

Cross	1	2	3	4	5	6	...	n	...	200
Number of squares	1	5	9				...		...	

Discovering Geometry Teacher's Resource Book
© 1997 by Key Curriculum Press. All rights reserved.
Transparency and Worksheet Masters/**13**

Exercises 8 and 9.

8.

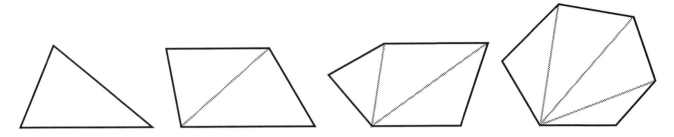

Number of diagonals from one vertex in a polygon

Sides	1	2	3	4	5	6	...	n	...	35
Diagonals from one vertex	⊠	⊠					...		...	
Triangles formed	⊠	⊠					...		...	

9.

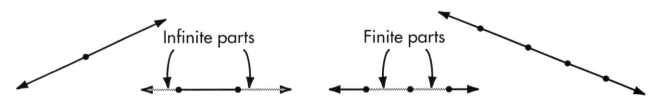

Infinite parts   Finite parts

Points dividing a line

Points dividing line	1	2	3	4	5	6	...	n	...	200
Infinite parts							...		...	
Finite parts (no overlap)							...		...	
Total parts							...		...	

Exercises 3 and 4.

3.

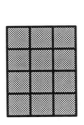

Squares in a rectangular array

Rectangle	1	2	3	4	5	6	...	n	...	200
Number of squares	6	12					...		...	

4.

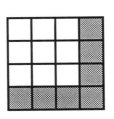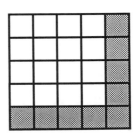

Shaded squares in a square array

Squares on a side	1	2	3	4	5	6	...	n	...	200
Shaded squares	1	3	5				...		...	
Unshaded squares	0	1	4				...		...	

Exercises 11, 12, and 31.

11.

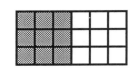

Shaded squares in a rectangular array

Rectangle	1	2	3	4	5	6	...	n	...	200
Shaded squares	2	5	9				...		...	

12.

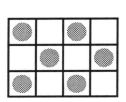

Dots in a rectangular array

Rectangle	1	2	3	4	5	6	...	n	...	200
Number of dots	3	6	10				...		...	

31.

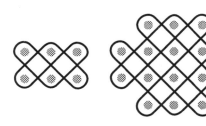

Lesson 1.6/Page 66

Exercises 1 and 2.

1.

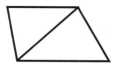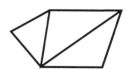

Number of diagonals from one vertex in a polygon

Sides	1	2	3	4	5	6	...	n	...	35
Diagonals from one vertex	✕	✕					...		...	

2.

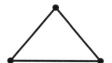

Line segments joining random points

Points	1	2	3	4	5	6	...	n	...	35
Line segments	0	1	3				...		...	

Exercises 3 and 4.

3.

 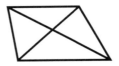  

Total number of diagonals in a polygon

Sides	1	2	3	4	5	6	...	n	...	35
Total diagonals	✕	✕	0	2			...		...	

4.

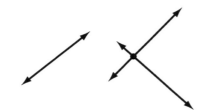 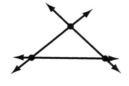 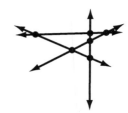

Intersecting random lines

Lines	1	2	3	4	5	6	...	n	...	35
Intersections	0	1					...		...	

17.

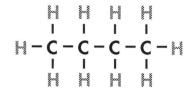

Methane	Ethane	Propane	Butane
(CH_4)	(C_2H_6)	(C_3H_8)	(C_4H_{10})

19.

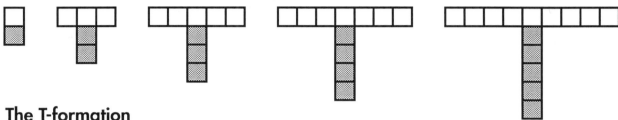

The T-formation

T		1	2	3	4	5	...
Number of shaded squares		1	2	3			...
Number of unshaded squares		1	3	5			...
Number of squares total							...

20.

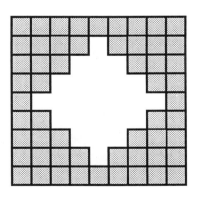

Missing cross pattern

Donut	1	2	3	4	5	6	...	n	...	200
Number of squares	8	20	36				...		...	

Exercises 5–8.

5.

 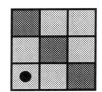 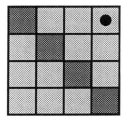

6.*

7.

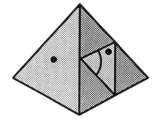 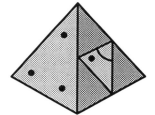 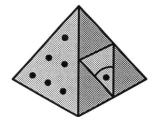

8.

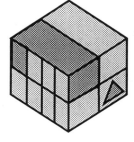 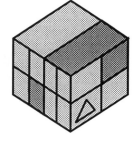 

Exercises 10 and 15.

10.

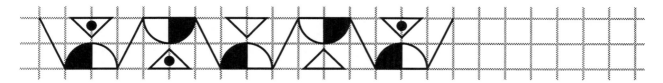

15.

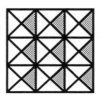
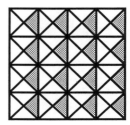

Triangles in a square array

Squares/side ·	1	2	3	4	5	6	…	n	…	35
Shaded Δs	1	4					…		…	
Unshaded Δs	3	12					…		…	

16.

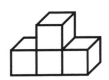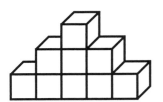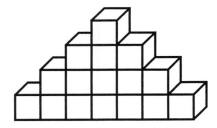

Building block pattern

Height	1	2	3	4	5	6	...	n	...	35
Total blocks	1	4					...		...	

17.

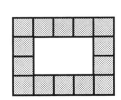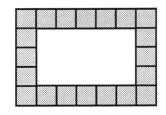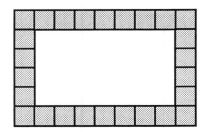

Rectangular donut pattern

Donut	1	2	3	4	5	...	n	...	35
Number of squares	8	14				...		...	

Definition List

space – The set of all points.

line segment – A line segment consists of two points and all the points between them that lie on the line containing the two points.

     ex: A ●——————● B $\overline{AB}$ or $\overline{BA}$

ray – A ray is part of a line that contains the starting point and all points on that ray that are on the same side of the starting point as the endpoint.

      O ●——●—→ P $\overrightarrow{OP}$

Exercises 1–10.

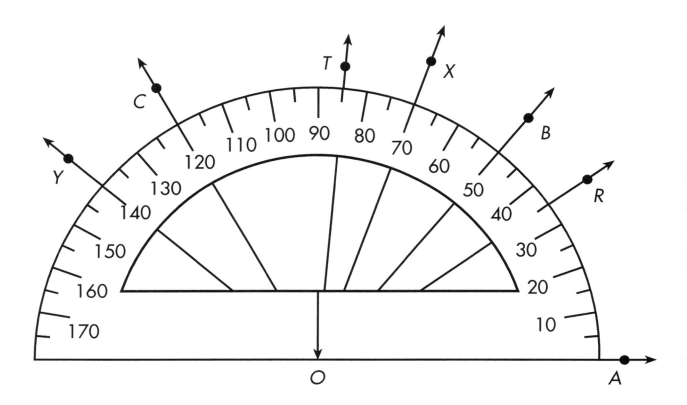

Exercises 26–28.

26.

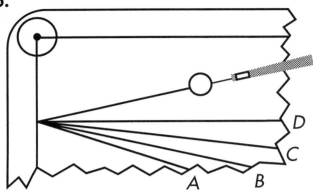

27.

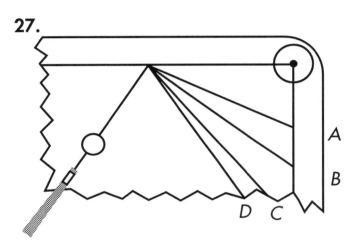

28.

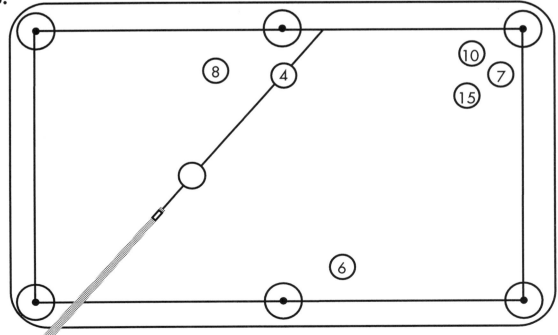

Example B

Orks

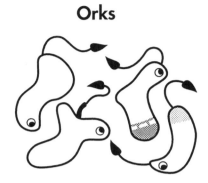

Not Orks

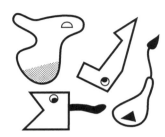

Who are Orks?

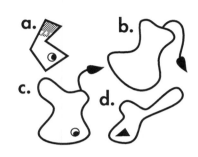

Investigation 2.3.1

Widgets

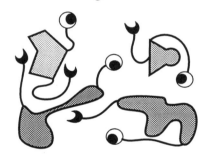

Not Widgets

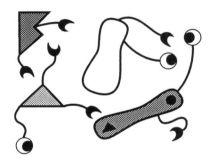

Who are Widgets?

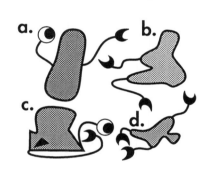

Zoids

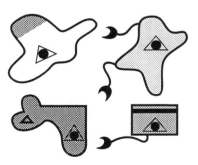

Not Zoids

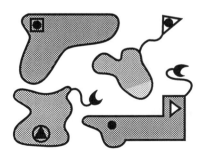

Who are Zoids?

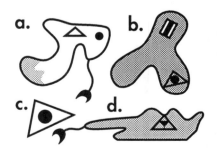

Exercises 30 and 31.

30.

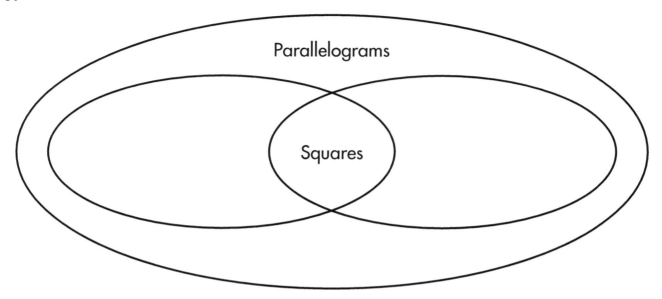

Venn diagram for parallelograms

31.

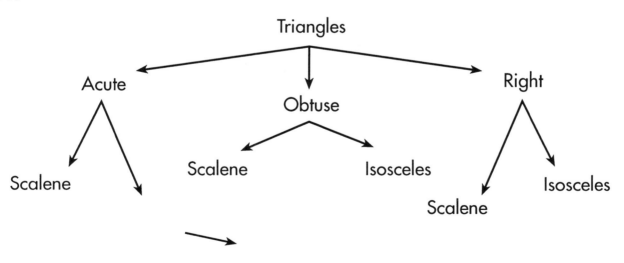

Tree diagram for triangles

Exercises 8–11.

8.

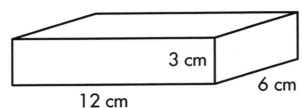

3 cm

6 cm

12 cm

9.

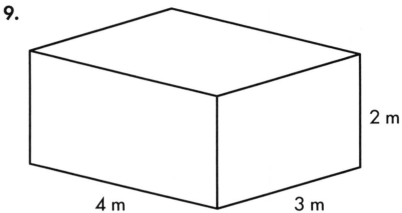

2 m

4 m   3 m

10.

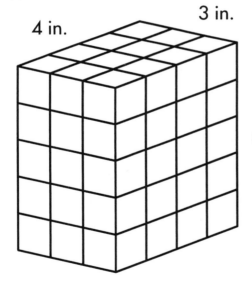

4 in.   3 in.

5 in.

11.

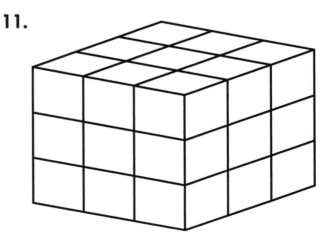

Exercise 11.

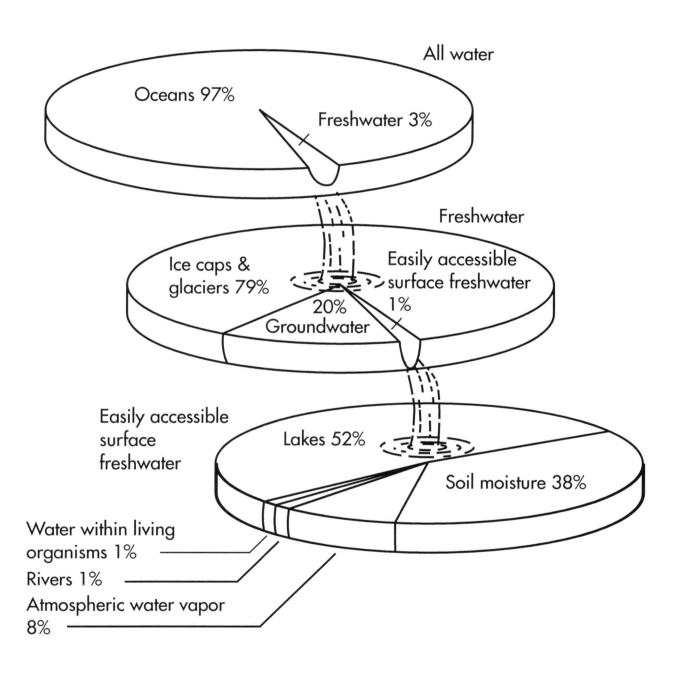

All water

Oceans 97%

Freshwater 3%

Freshwater

Ice caps & glaciers 79%

Easily accessible surface freshwater 1%

20% Groundwater

Easily accessible surface freshwater

Lakes 52%

Soil moisture 38%

Water within living organisms 1%

Rivers 1%

Atmospheric water vapor 8%

Exercise 12.

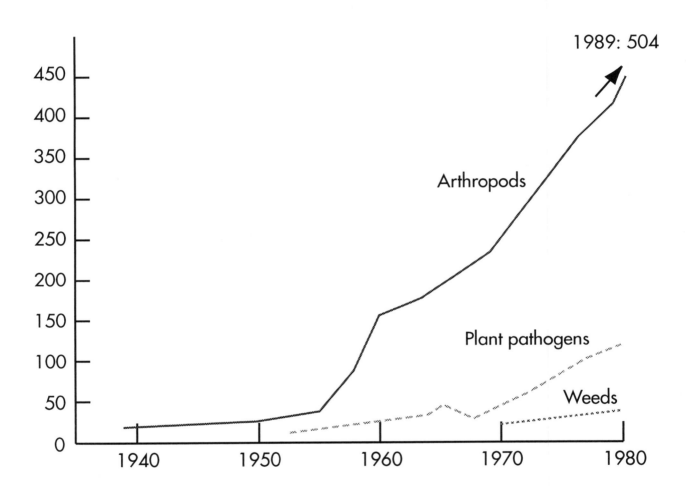

Exercises 44–49.

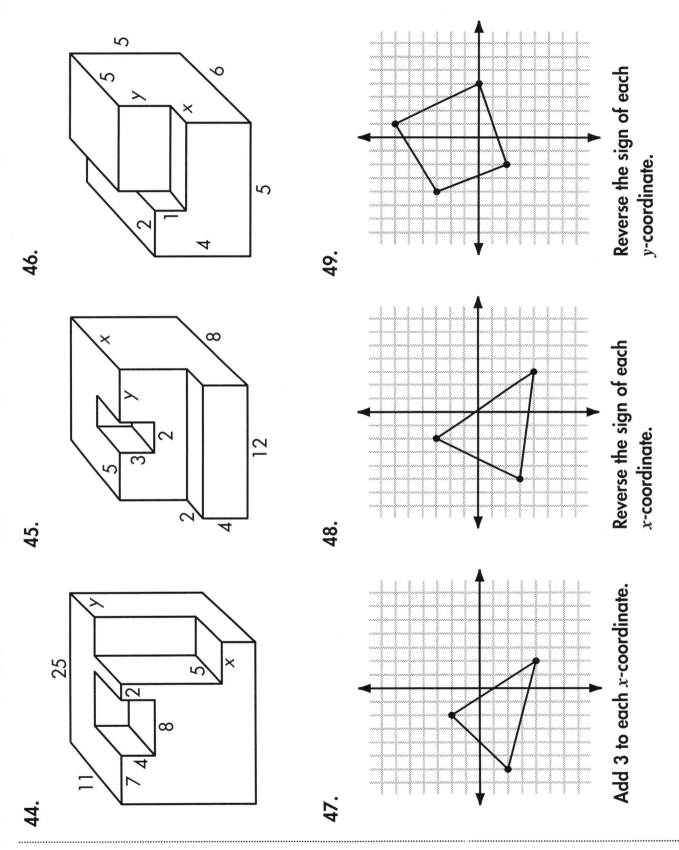

46.

45.

44.

49. Reverse the sign of each *y*-coordinate.

48. Reverse the sign of each *x*-coordinate.

47. Add 3 to each *x*-coordinate.

Exercises 18 and 19.

18.

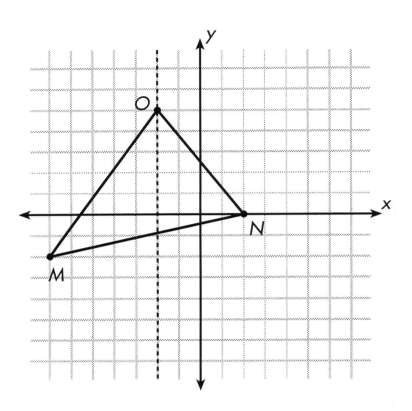

19.

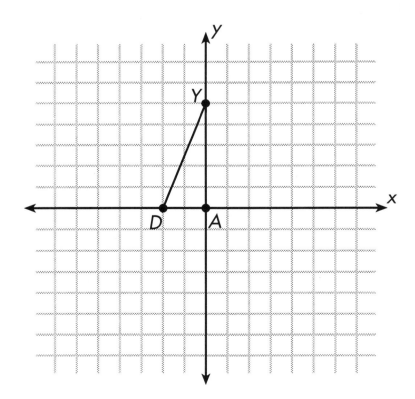

Exercise 4.

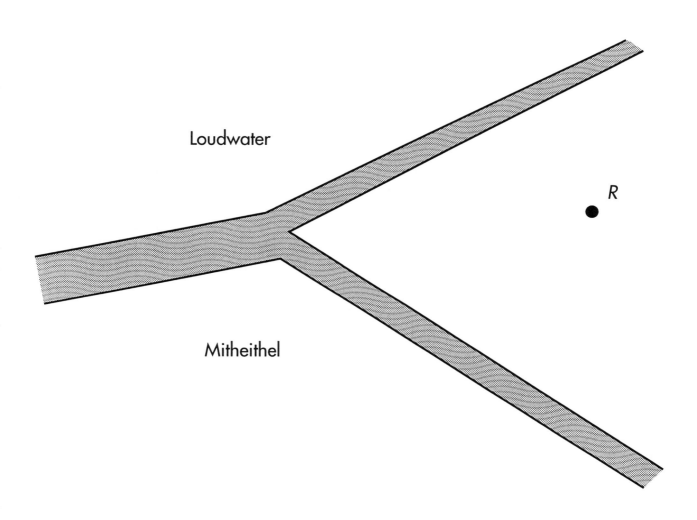

Loudwater

Mitheithel

R

Exercises 12 and 13.

12.

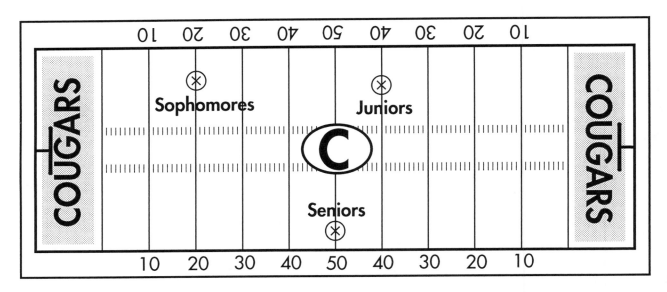

13.

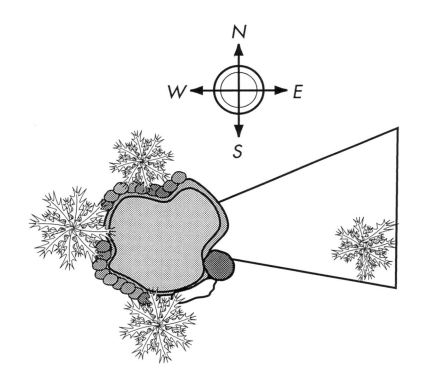

Exercises 11–13.

11.

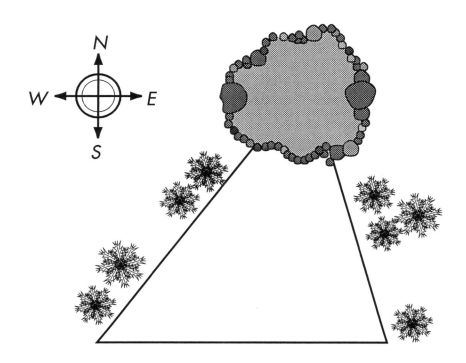

12.

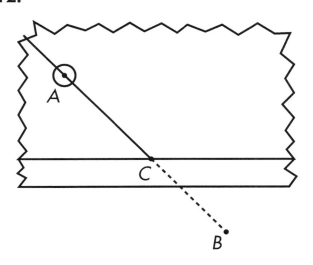

13.

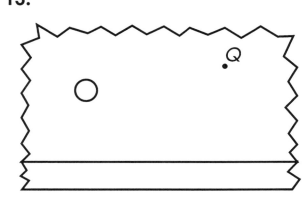

Exercises 1–5.

1.

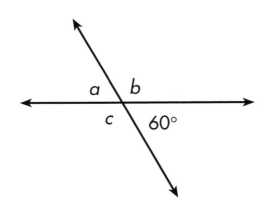

2.

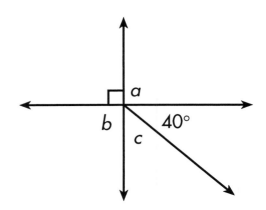

3.

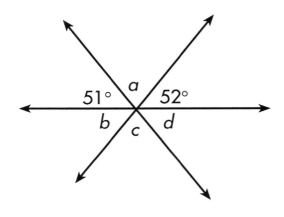

4.

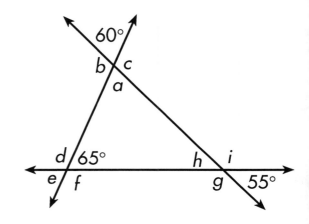

5.

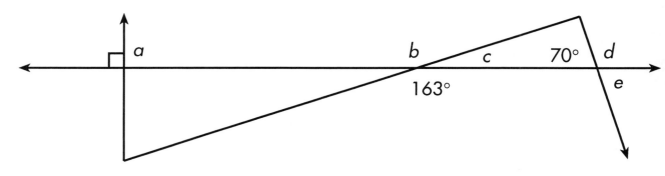

Discovering Geometry Teacher's Resource Book
© 1997 by Key Curriculum Press. All rights reserved.

Exercise 9.

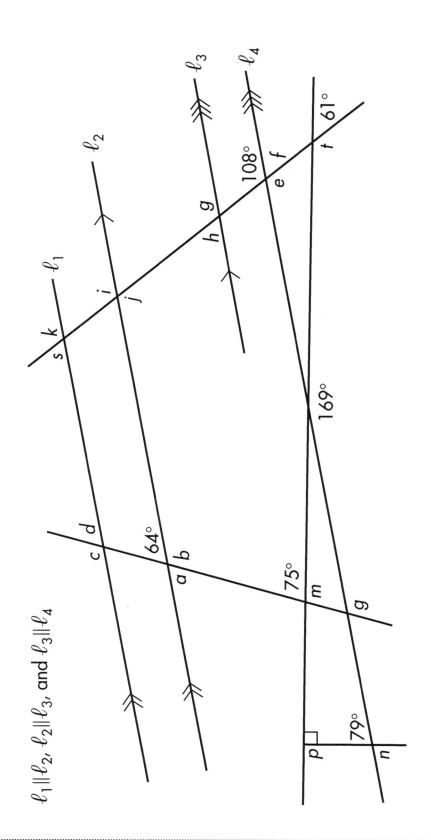

Project: Finding Treasure with Coordinates   W

Location of your buried treasure: This is where you hide your treasure and record your opponent's attempts to find your treasure.

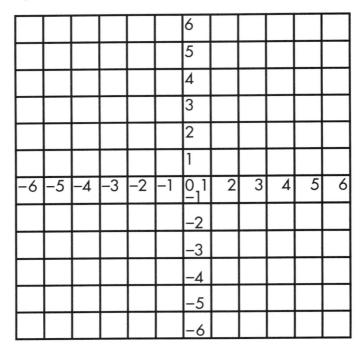

Location of your opponent's treasure: This is where you record your attempts to locate your opponent's treasure.

Location of your buried treasure: This is where you hide your treasure and record your opponent's attempts to find your treasure.

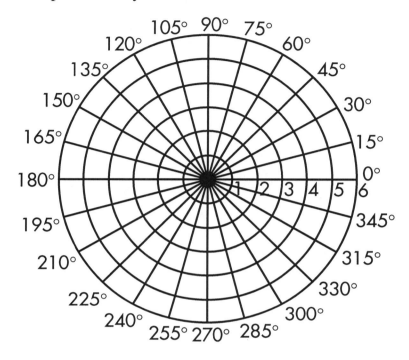

Location of your opponent's treasure: This is where you record your attempts to locate your opponent's treasure.

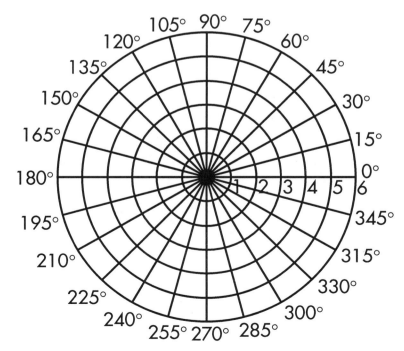

Exercise 25.

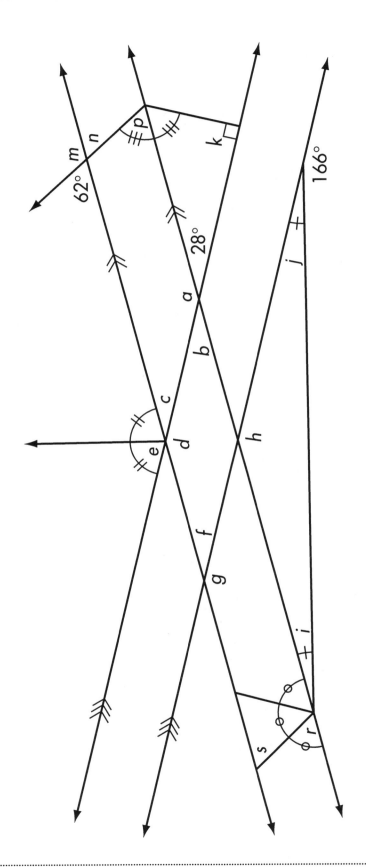

Exercises 7 and 8.

7.

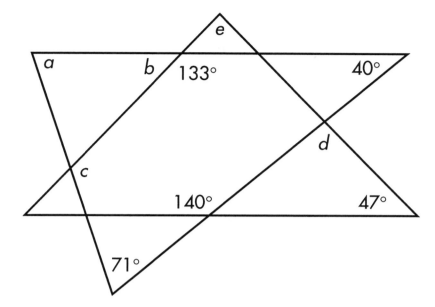

8.

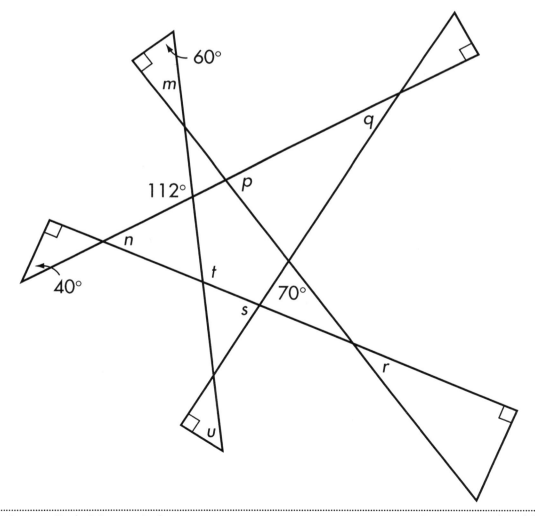

Exercises 7 and 8.

7.

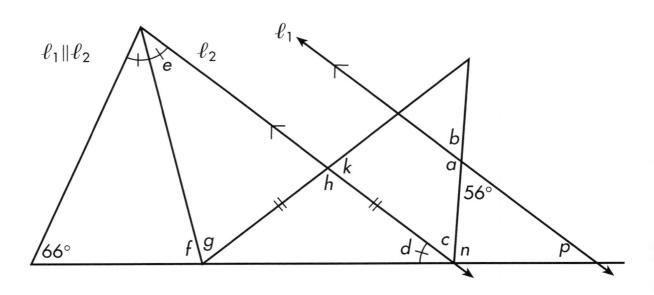

8.

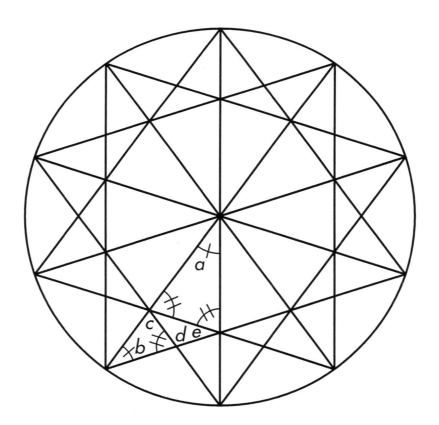

Exercises 19–21.

20. $(x, y) \rightarrow (x, -y)$

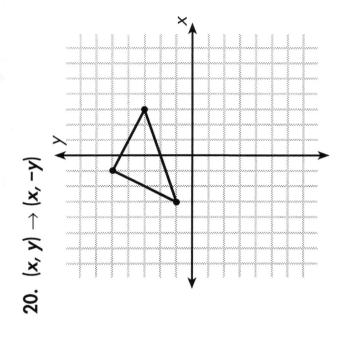

21. $(x, y) \rightarrow (y, x)$

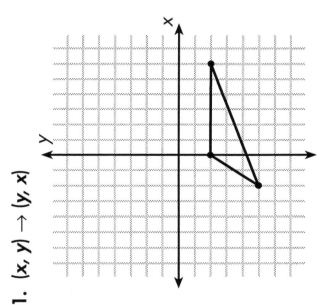

19.* $(x, y) \rightarrow (x + 5, y - 3)$

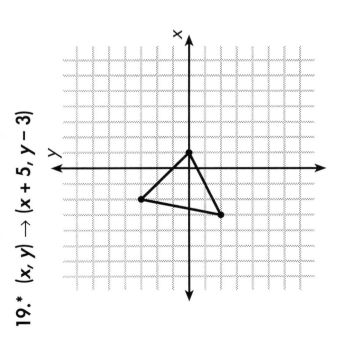

Exercise 21.

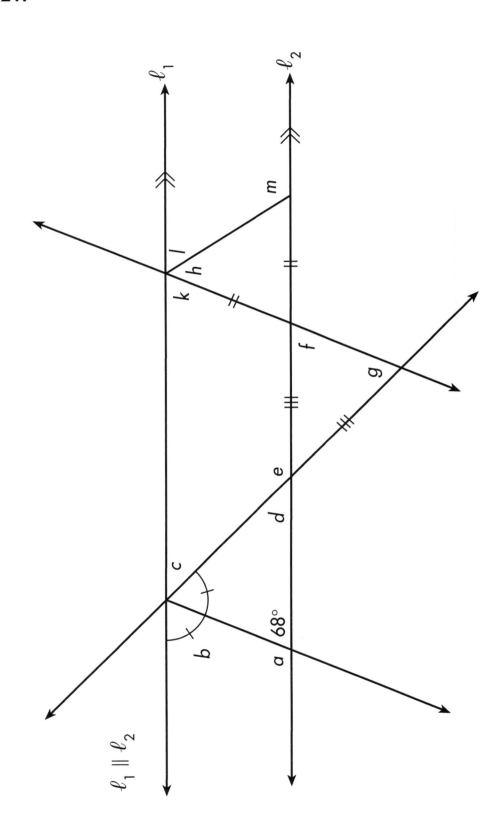

Exercise 23.

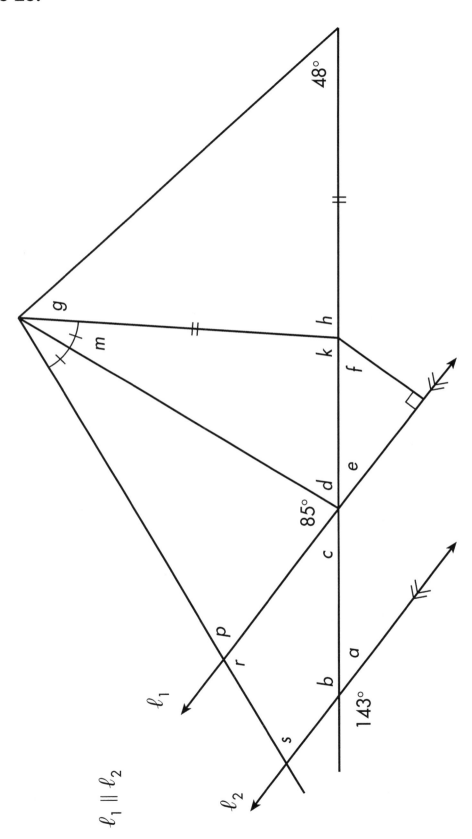

Exercise 10.

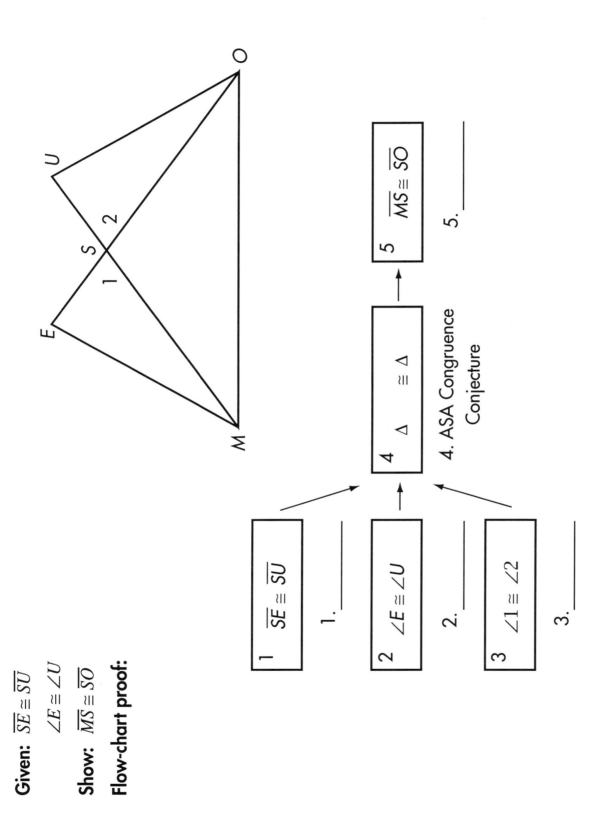

Given: $\overline{SE} \cong \overline{SU}$

        $\angle E \cong \angle U$

Show: $\overline{MS} \cong \overline{SO}$

Flow-chart proof:

Exercise 11.

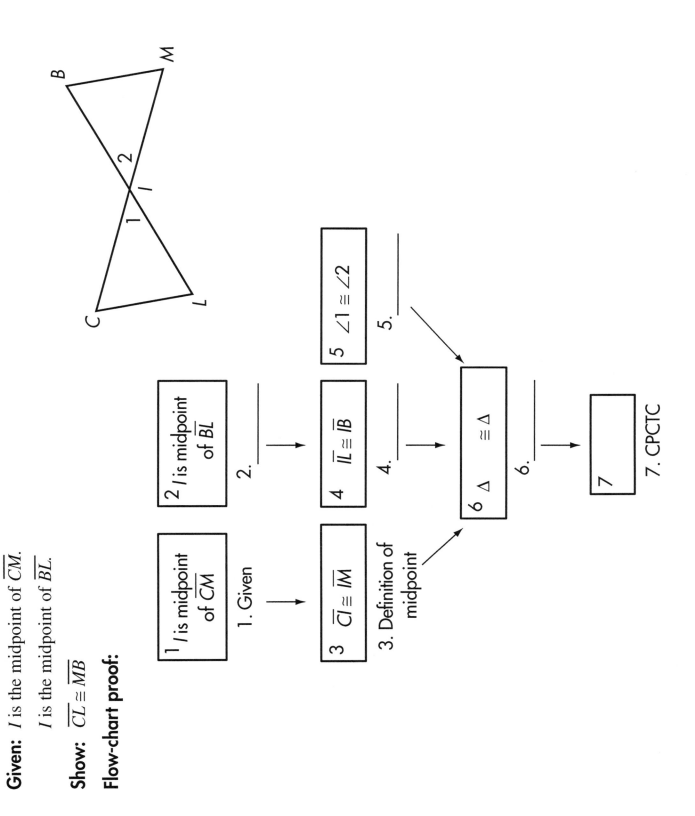

Given: *I* is the midpoint of $\overline{CM}$.

I is the midpoint of $\overline{BL}$.

Show: $\overline{CL} \cong \overline{MB}$

Flow-chart proof:

1. *I* is midpoint of $\overline{CM}$ — 1. Given

2. *I* is midpoint of $\overline{BL}$ — 2. _____

3. $\overline{CI} \cong \overline{IM}$ — 3. Definition of midpoint

4. $\overline{IL} \cong \overline{IB}$ — 4. _____

5. $\angle 1 \cong \angle 2$ — 5. _____

6. $\triangle \cong \triangle$ — 6. _____

7. — 7. CPCTC

Exercise 12.

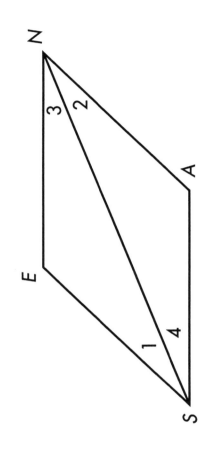

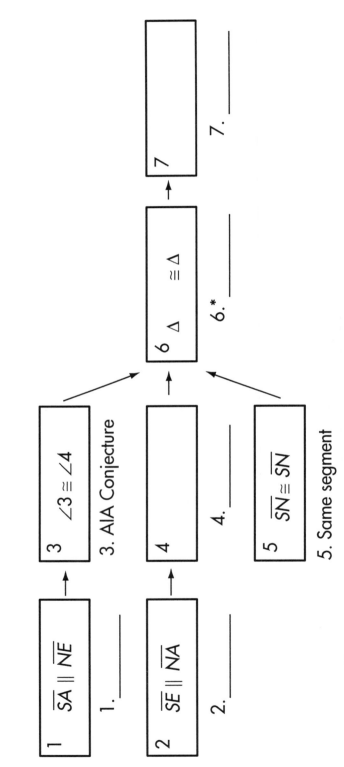

Given: $\overline{SA} \parallel \overline{NE}$
$\overline{SE} \parallel \overline{NA}$

Show: $\overline{SA} \cong \overline{NE}$

Flow-chart proof:

1 | $\overline{SA} \parallel \overline{NE}$
1. _____

2 | $\overline{SE} \parallel \overline{NA}$
2. _____

3 | $\angle 3 \cong \angle 4$
3. AIA Conjecture

4 |
4. _____

5 | $\overline{SN} \cong \overline{SN}$
5. Same segment

6 | $\triangle \quad \cong \triangle$
6.* _____

7 |
7. _____

Exercise 17.

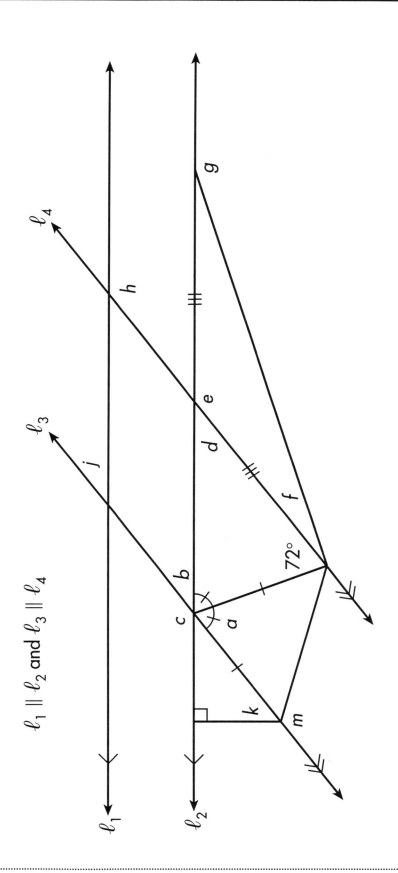

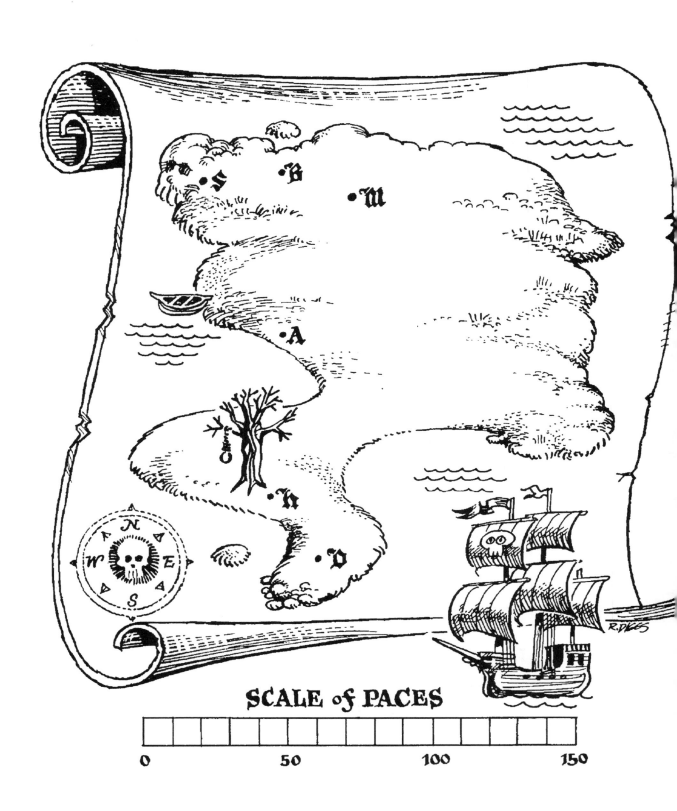

SCALE of PACES

| 0 | 50 | 100 | 150 |

Exercise 7.

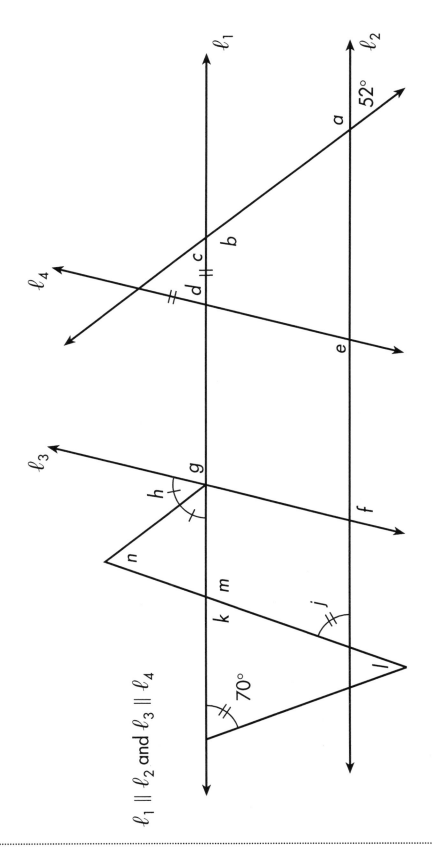

Exercise 11.

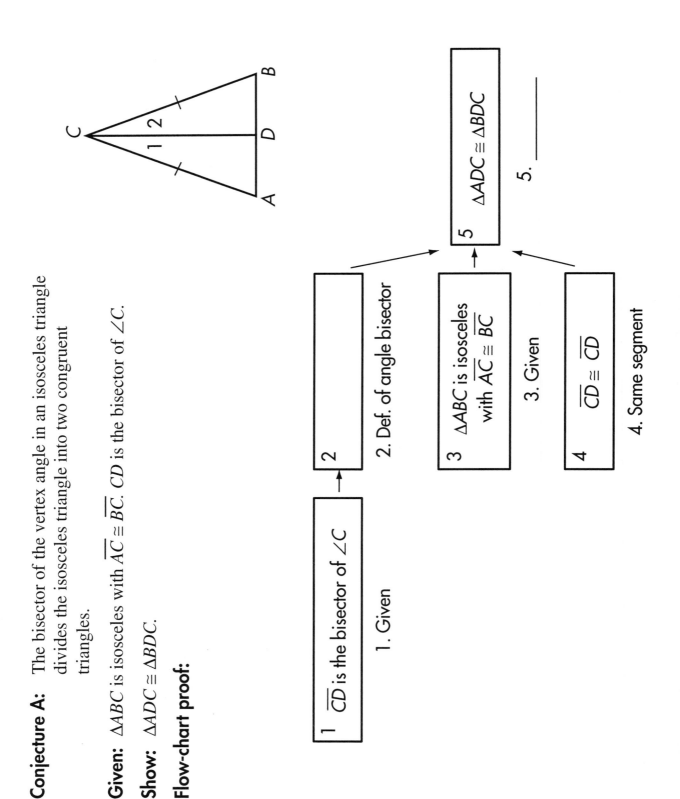

Conjecture A: The bisector of the vertex angle in an isosceles triangle divides the isosceles triangle into two congruent triangles.

Given: $\triangle ABC$ is isosceles with $\overline{AC} \cong \overline{BC}$. $\overline{CD}$ is the bisector of $\angle C$.

Show: $\triangle ADC \cong \triangle BDC$.

Flow-chart proof:

1 $\overline{CD}$ is the bisector of $\angle C$

1. Given

2

2. Def. of angle bisector

3 $\triangle ABC$ is isosceles with $\overline{AC} \cong \overline{BC}$

3. Given

4 $\overline{CD} \cong \overline{CD}$

4. Same segment

5 $\triangle ADC \cong \triangle BDC$

5. _____

Exercise 12.

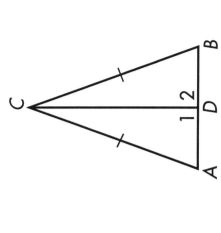

Conjecture B: The bisector of the vertex angle in an isosceles triangle is also the altitude to the base.

Given: △ABC is isosceles with $\overline{AC} \cong \overline{BC}$. $\overline{CD}$ is the bisector of ∠C.

Show: $\overline{CD}$ is an altitude.

Flow-chart proof:

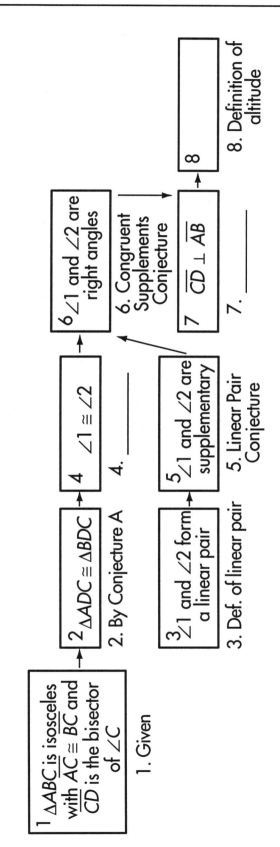

1 △ABC is isosceles with $\overline{AC} \cong \overline{BC}$ and $\overline{CD}$ is the bisector of ∠C

1. Given

2 △ADC ≅ △BDC

2. By Conjecture A

3 ∠1 and ∠2 form a linear pair

3. Def. of linear pair

4 ∠1 ≅ ∠2

4. _____

5 ∠1 and ∠2 are supplementary

5. Linear Pair Conjecture

6 ∠1 and ∠2 are right angles

6. Congruent Supplements Conjecture

7 $\overline{CD} \perp \overline{AB}$

7. _____

8

8. Definition of altitude

Exercises 44 and 48.

44.

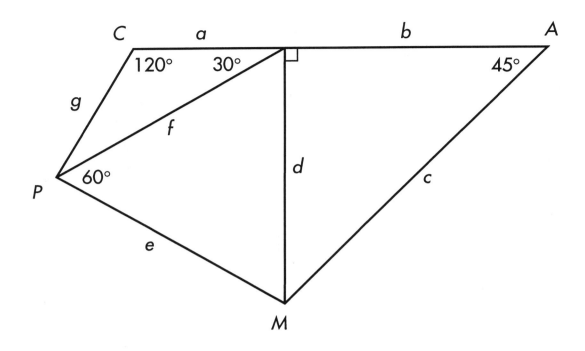

48.

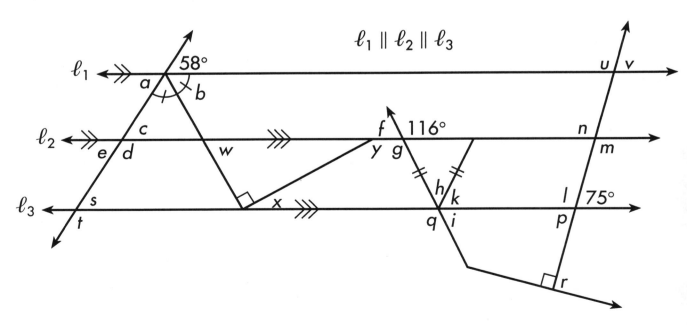

Discovering Geometry Teacher's Resource Book

Exercise 7.

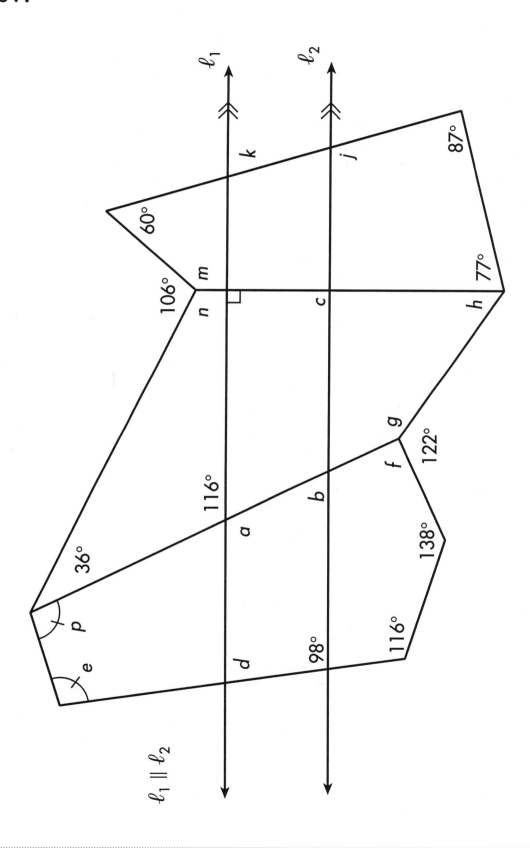

Exercise 8.

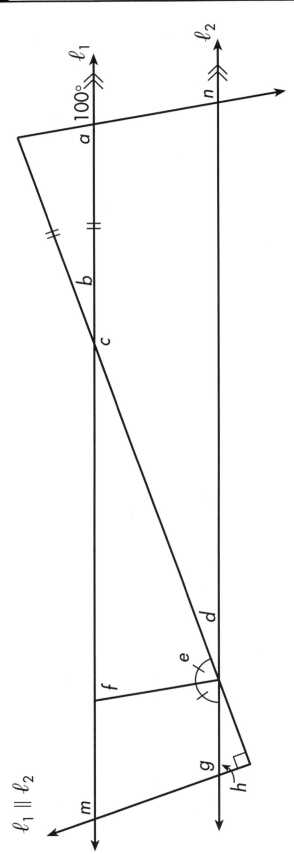

Exercise 18.

Given: Isosceles trapezoid with $\overline{AB} \cong \overline{DC}$

Show: $\overline{AC} \cong \overline{DB}$

Flow-chart proof:

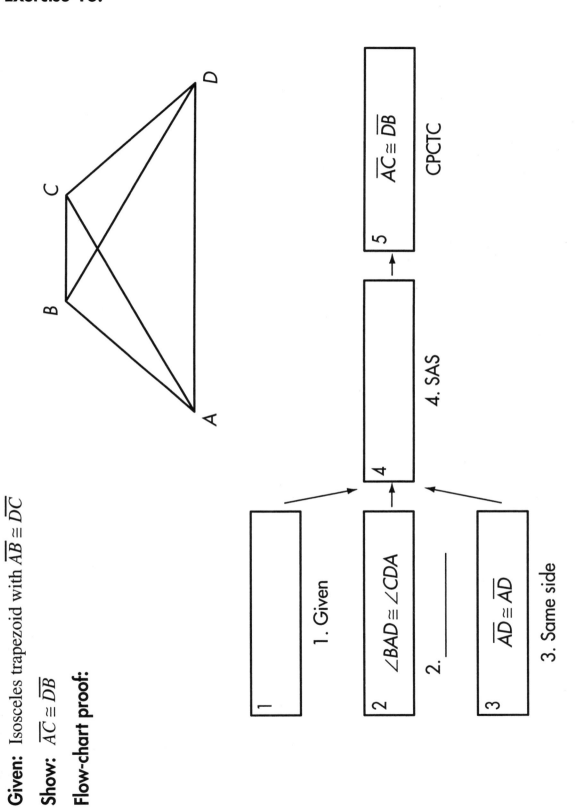

Exercises 7 and 17.

7.

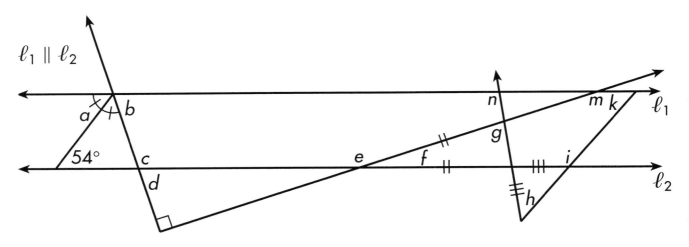

17.

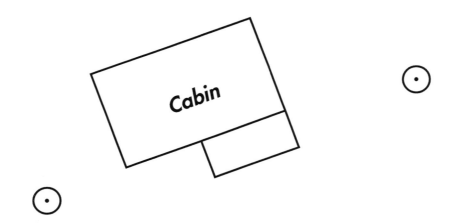

Discovering Geometry Teacher's Resource Book

Exercises 14 and 15.

15.

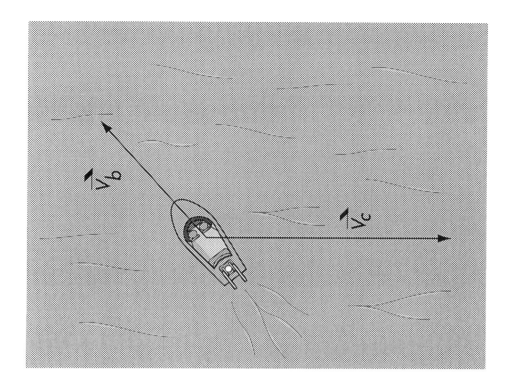

14.

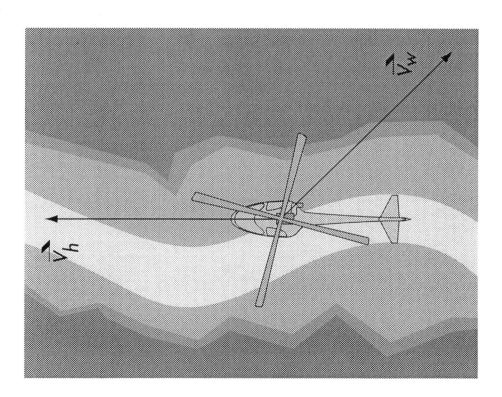

Exercise 16.

Given: *LEAN* is a parallelogram.

Show: $\overline{EN}$ and $\overline{LA}$ bisect each other.

Flow-chart proof:

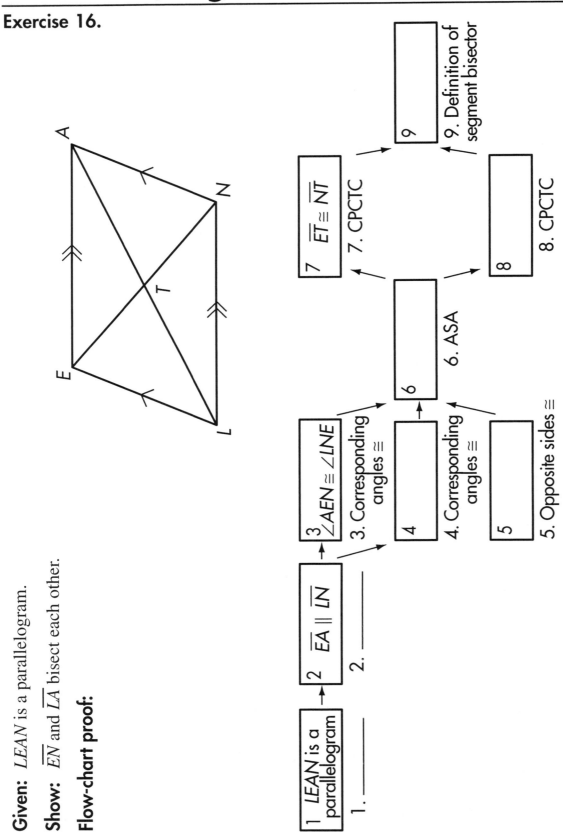

1 *LEAN* is a parallelogram

1. _____

2 $\overline{EA} \parallel \overline{LN}$

2. _____

3 $\angle AEN \cong \angle LNE$

3. Corresponding angles $\cong$

4   4. Corresponding angles $\cong$

5   5. Opposite sides $\cong$

6   6. ASA

7 $\overline{ET} \cong \overline{NT}$

7. CPCTC

8   8. CPCTC

9   9. Definition of segment bisector

Exercise 7.

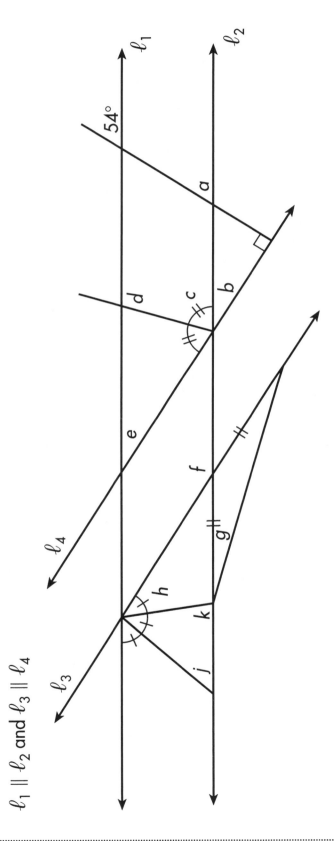

Exercise 21.

	Kite	Isosceles trapezoid	Parallelogram	Rhombus	Rectangle
Each pair of opposite sides ∥					
Opposite sides ≅					
Opposite ∠'s ≅					
Diagonals bisect each other					
Diagonals ⊥					
Diagonals ≅				No	
Exactly one line of symmetry	Yes				
Exactly two lines of symmetry					

Exercises 1–14.

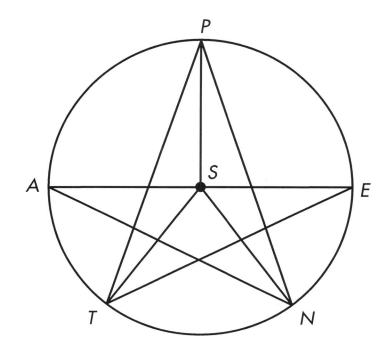

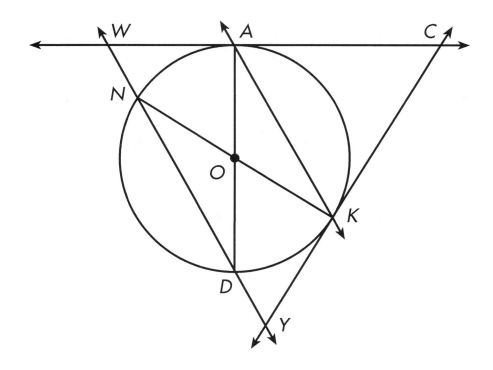

Exercises 14 and 15.

14.

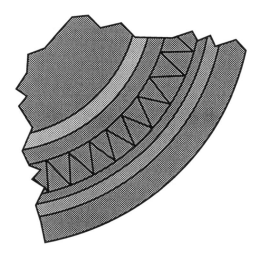

15.

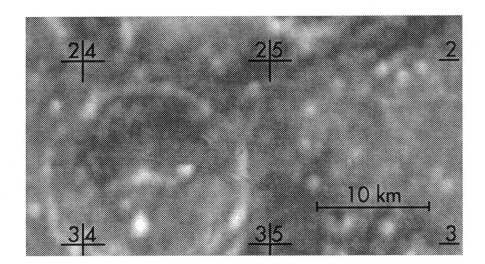

Exercise 20.

Given: Circle O with chords $\overline{AB} \cong \overline{CD}$.

Show: $\angle AOB \cong \angle COD$

Flow-chart proof:

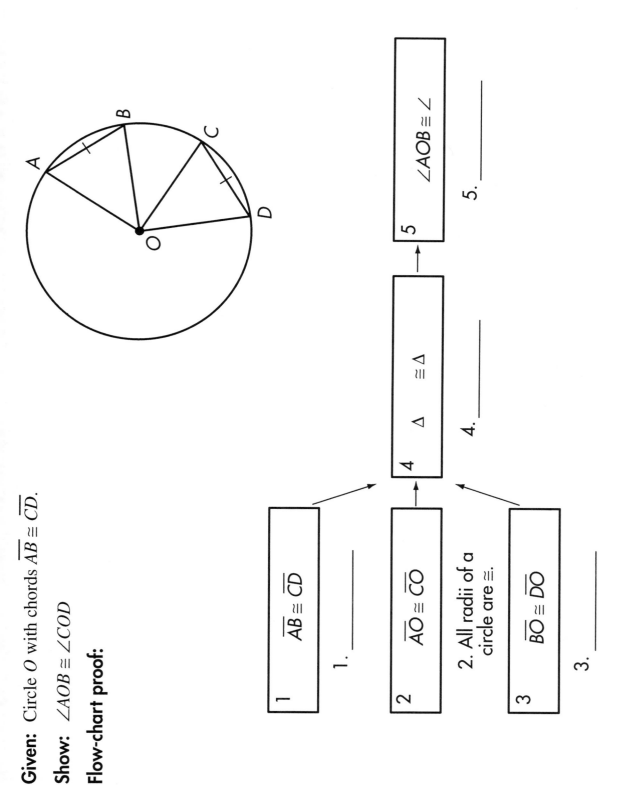

1 | $\overline{AB} \cong \overline{CD}$
1. _____

2 | $\overline{AO} \cong \overline{CO}$
2. All radii of a circle are $\cong$.

3 | $\overline{BO} \cong \overline{DO}$
3. _____

4 | $\triangle \_\_\_ \cong \triangle \_\_\_$
4. _____

5 | $\angle AOB \cong \angle \_\_\_$
5. _____

Exercise 17.

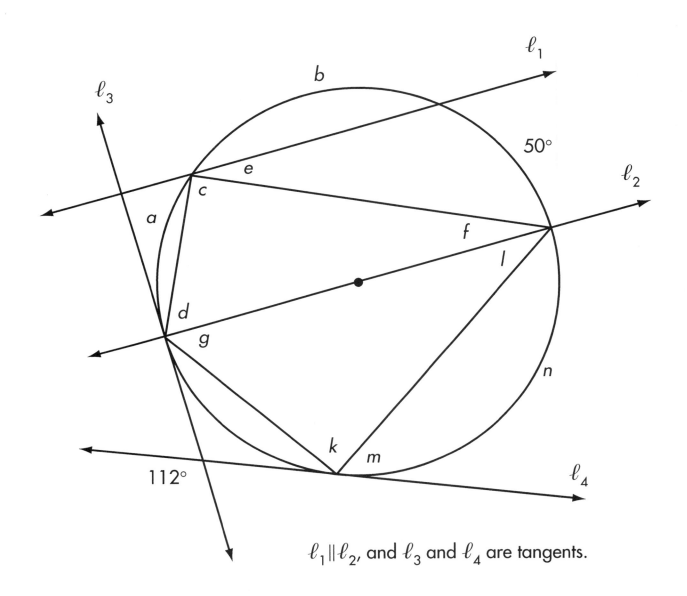

$\ell_1 \| \ell_2$, and ℓ_3 and ℓ_4 are tangents.

Exercise 14.

ℓ_1 and ℓ_2 are tangents.

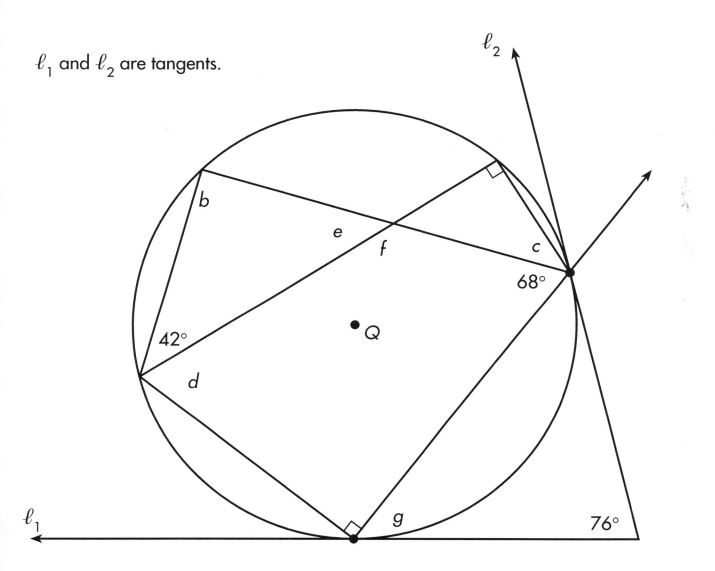

Exercises 35 and 38.

35.

Given: Circle M and circle S intersect at points A and T with radii $\overline{MS} \cong \overline{MT}$ and $\overline{SA} \cong \overline{ST}$.

Show: $\overline{MS}$ is the perpendicular bisector of $\overline{AT}$.

Flow-chart proof:

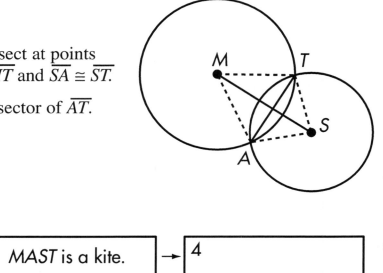

1

1. Given

2

2. Given

3   MAST is a kite.

3. _____

4

4. _____

38.

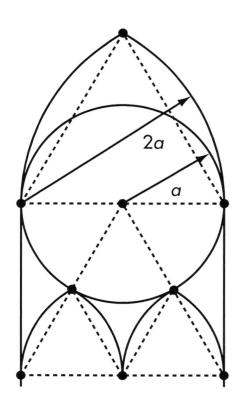

Exercises 1–4.

1.

2.

3.

4.

Exercises 11 and 12.

11.

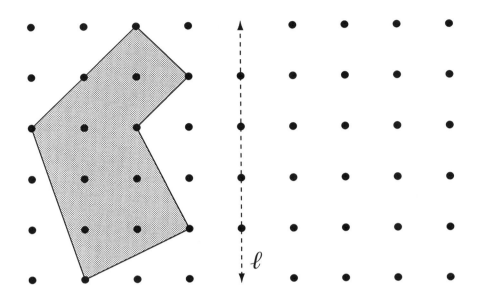

12.

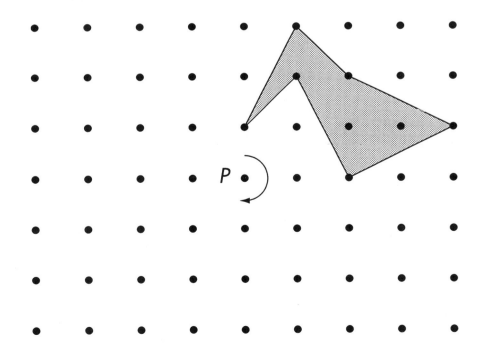

Discovering Geometry Teacher's Resource Book

Exercises 15 and 17.

15.

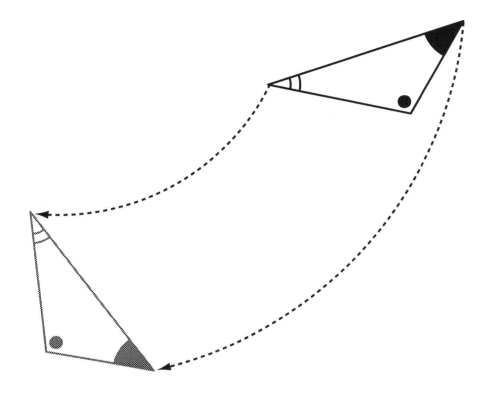

17.

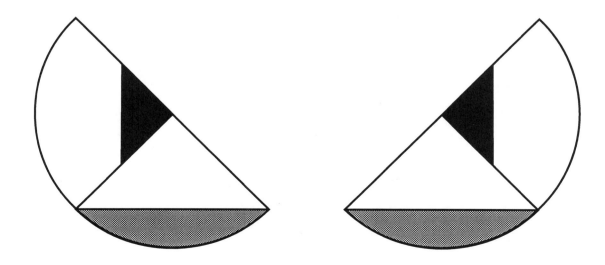

Exercises 1 and 2.

1.

2.

Exercises 13 and 14.

13.

14.

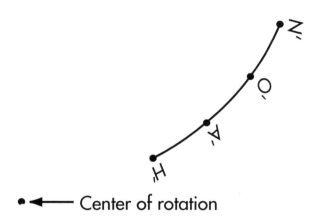

Center of rotation

Exercises 15 and 16.

15.

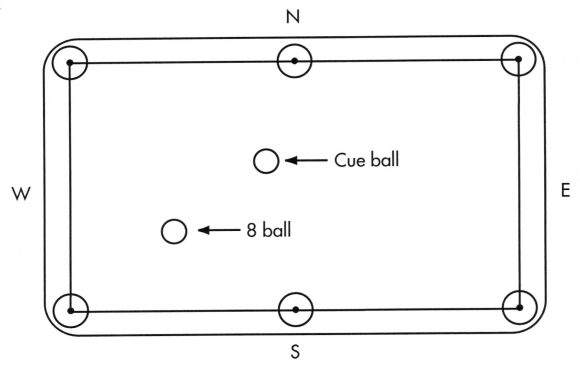

16.

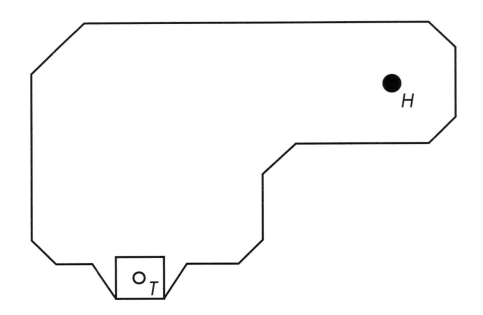

Exercises 21 and 22.

21.

22.

Investigation 8.4.

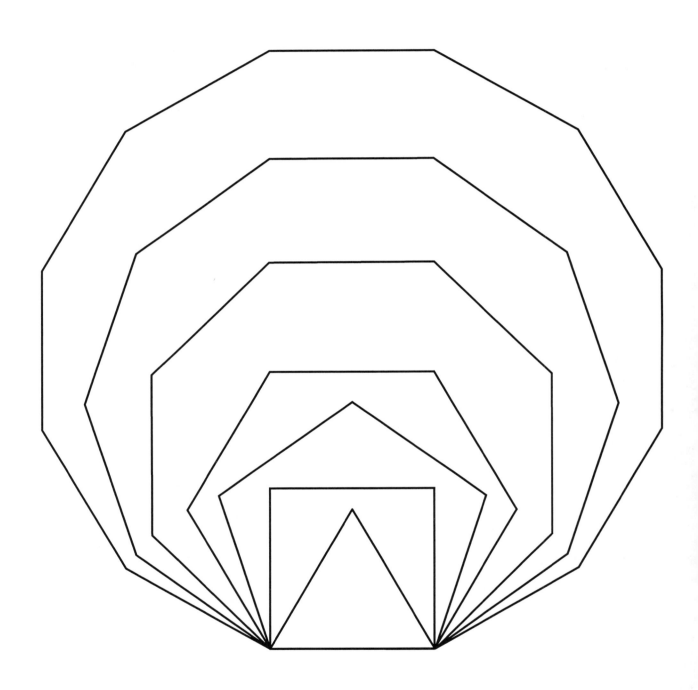

Investigation 8.4.

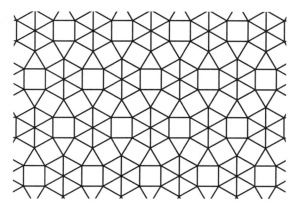

$3^6/3^2.4.3.4$

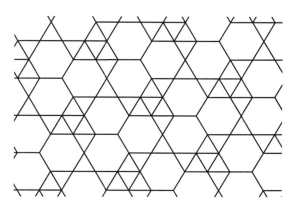

$3^4.6/3^2.6^2/3.6.3.6/6^3$

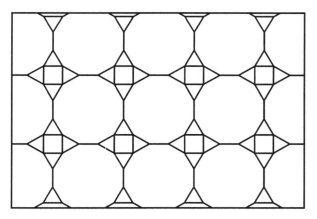

$3.4.3.12/3.12^2$

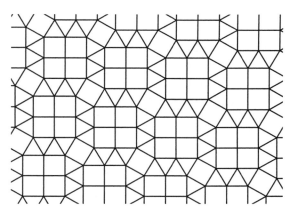

$3^3.4^2/3^2.4.3.4/4^4$

Exercises 3–5 and 9–11.

3.

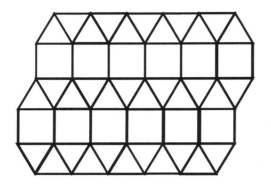

4.

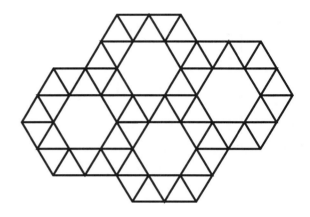

5.

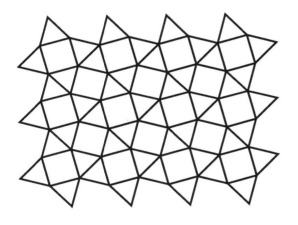

9.

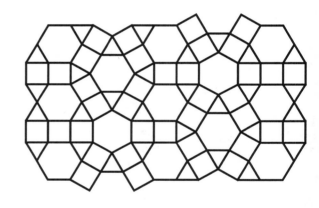

10.

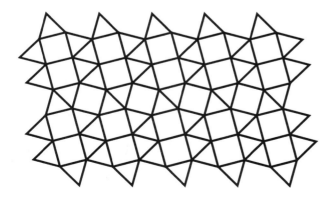

11.

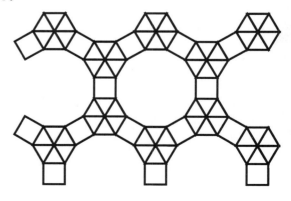

Exercises 19 and 20.

19.

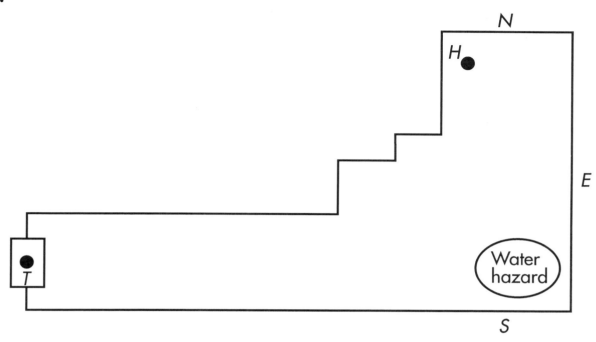

20.

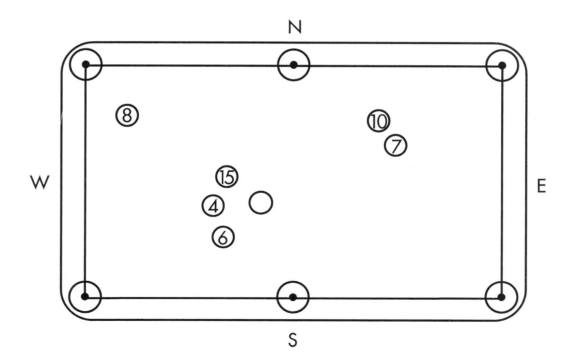

Exercise 8.

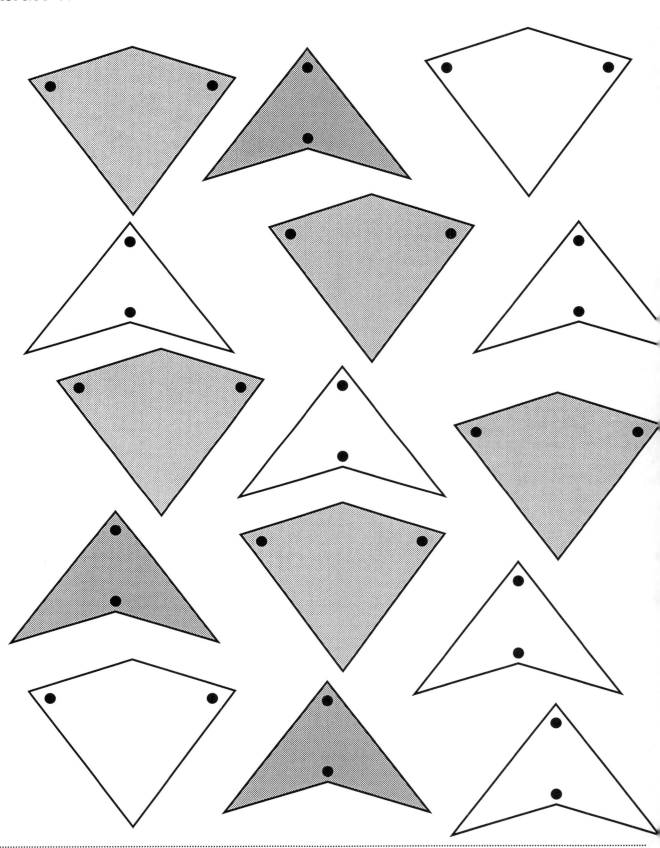

Exercises 7 and 8.

7.

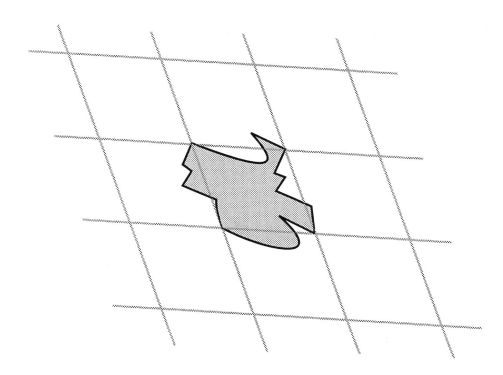

8.

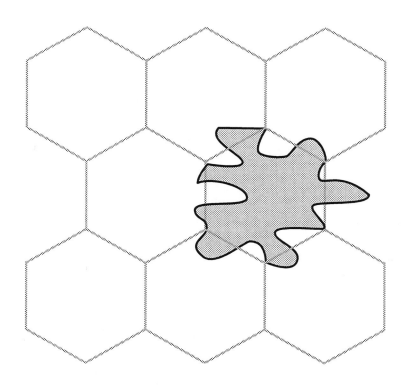

Exercises 3, 4, and 8.

3.

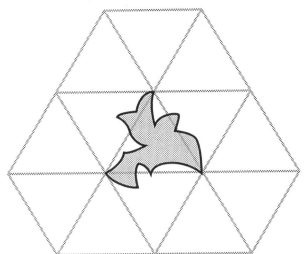

4.

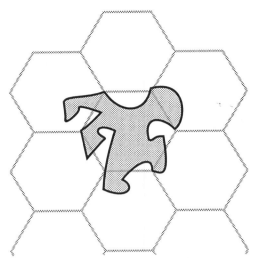

8.

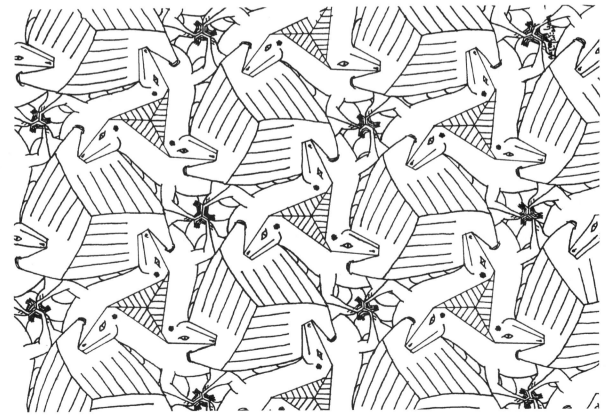

Garret Lum, geometry student

Exercises 3 and 4.

3.

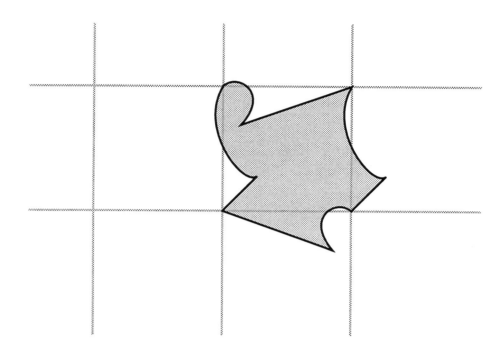

4.

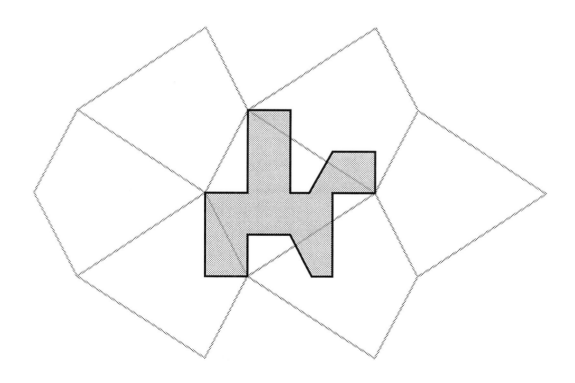

Exercises 20-22.

20.

21.

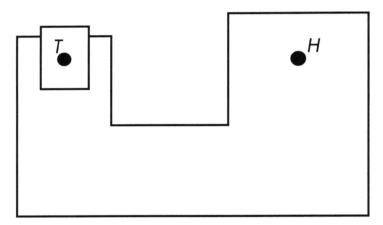

22.

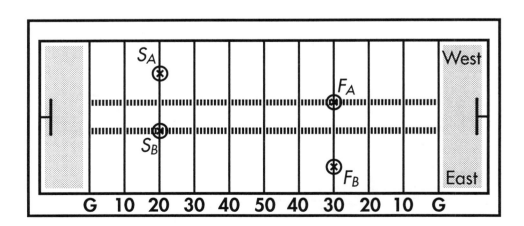

Exercises 1–4.

1.

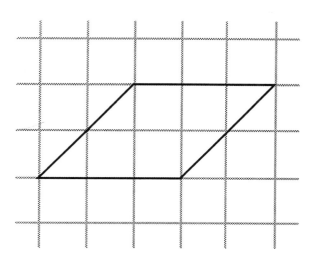

2.

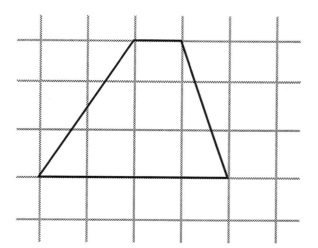

3.

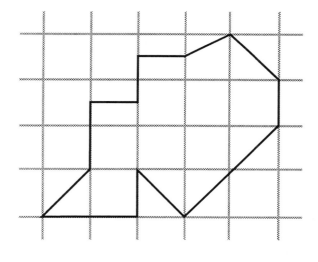

4.

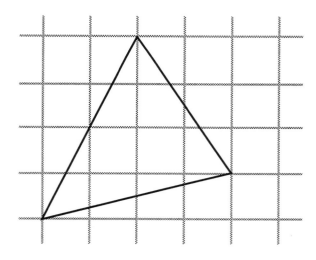

Japanese Puzzle Quilt Grid.

Investigation 9.3.

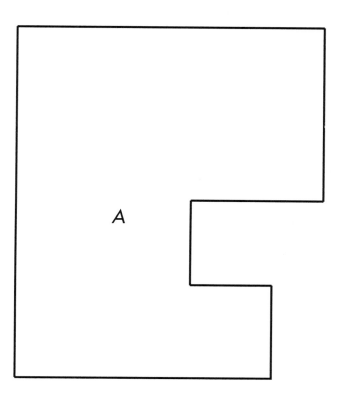

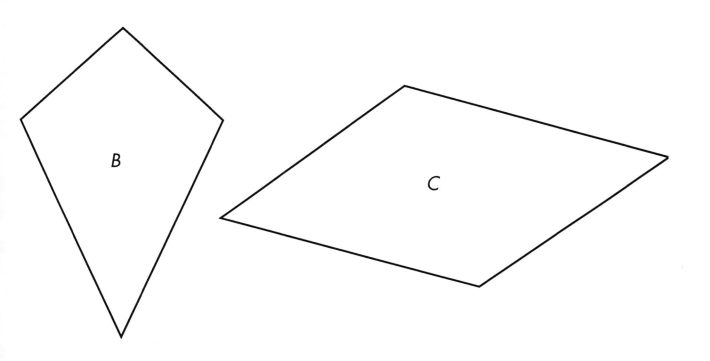

Investigation 9.3.

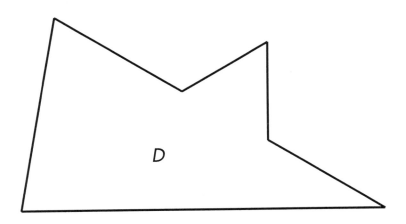

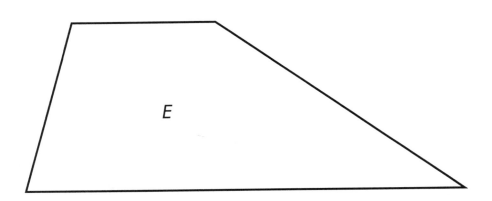

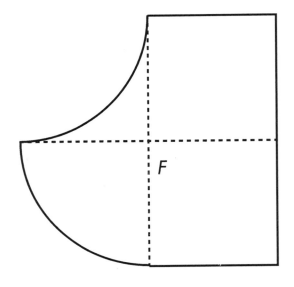

Investigation 9.3.

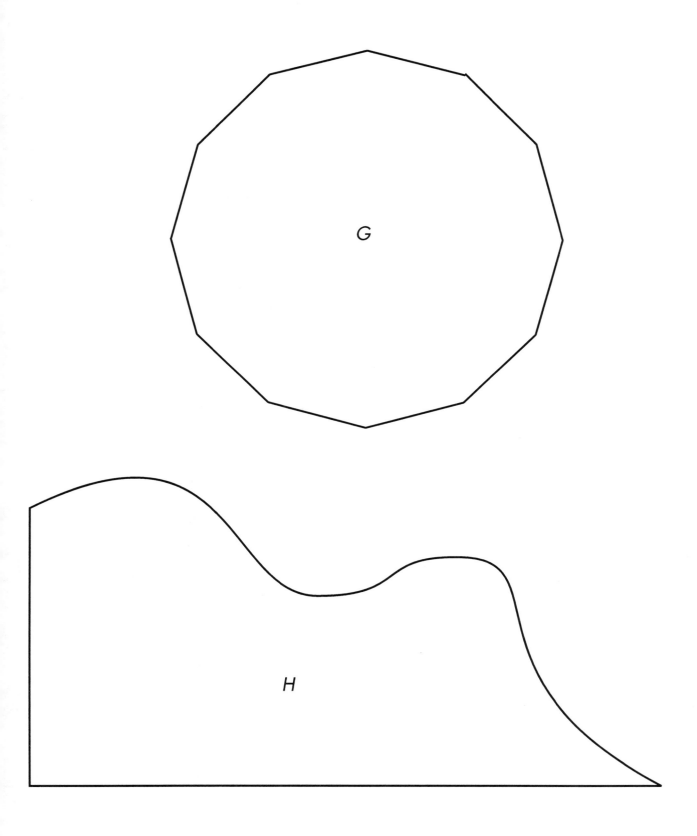

G

H

Exercises 14–17.

14.

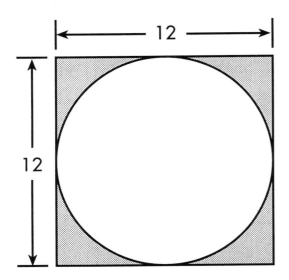

15.

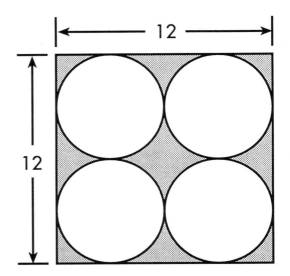

16.

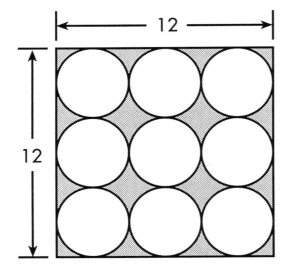

17.

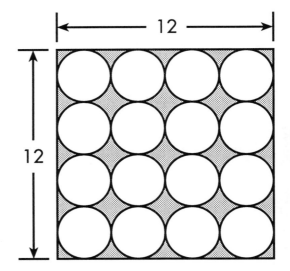

Exercise 19.

a.

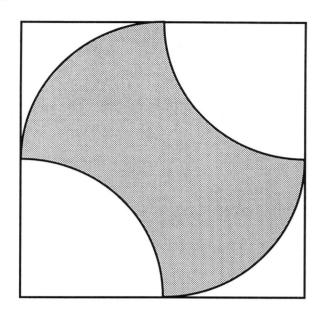

b.

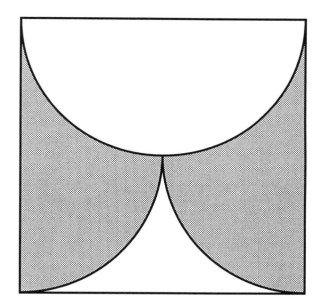

c.

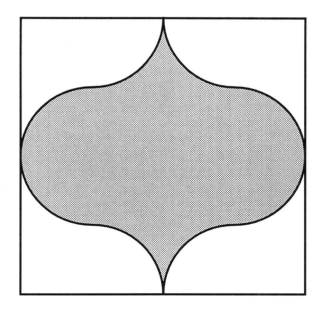

d.

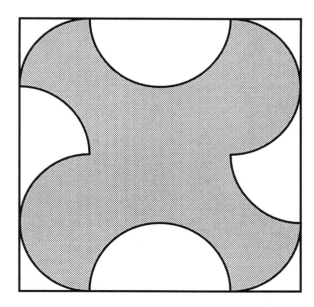

Exercise 12.

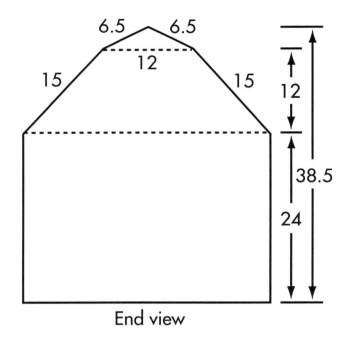

End view

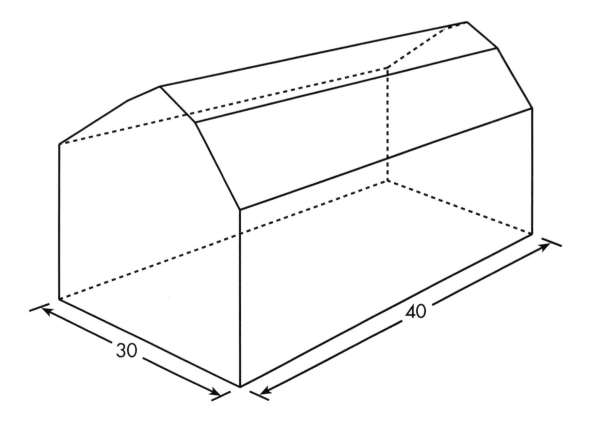

Discovering Geometry Teacher's Resource Book

Exercises 31 and 32.

31.

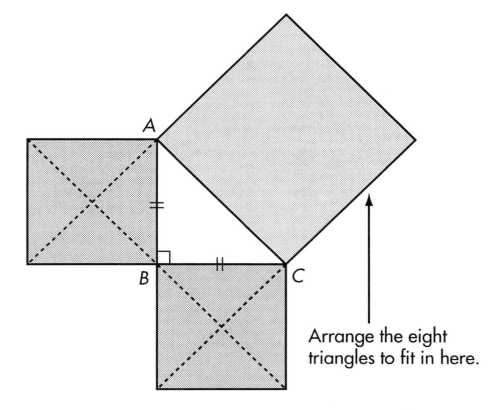

Arrange the eight
triangles to fit in here.

32.

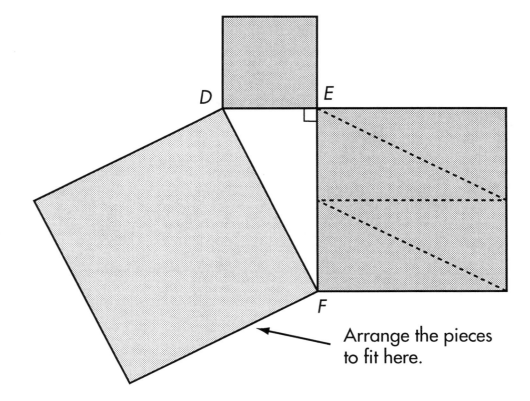

Arrange the pieces
to fit here.

Exercises 46–49.

46.

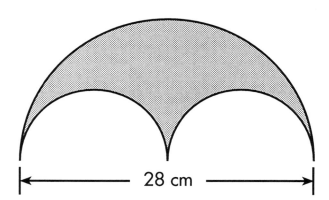

47.*

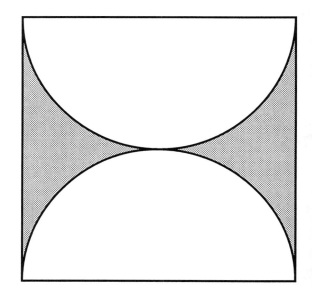

48.

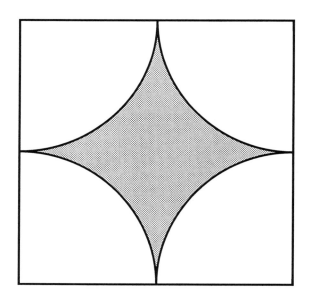

49.

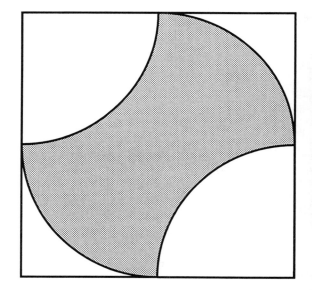

Investigation 10.1.

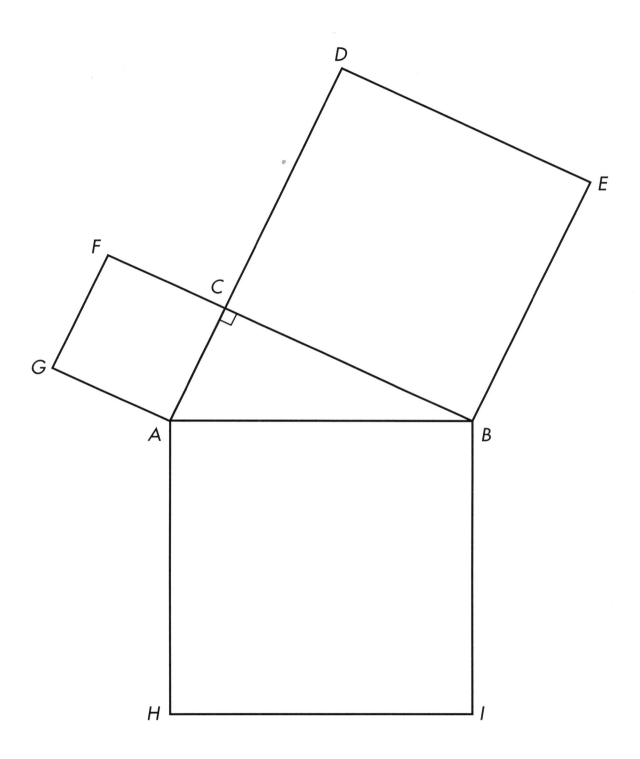

Square grid.

Isometric grid.

Exercise 6.

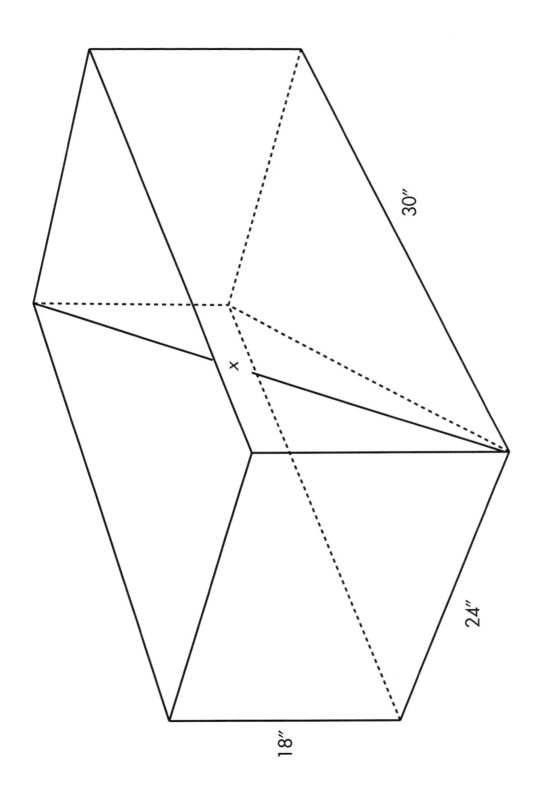

1.

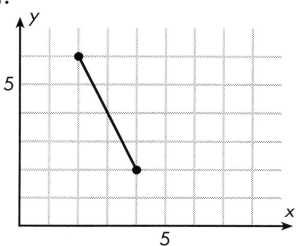

2.

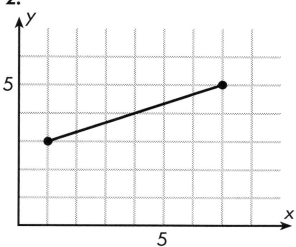

3.

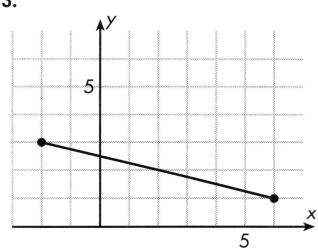

4.*

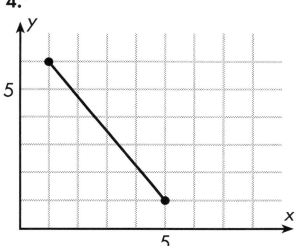

5.

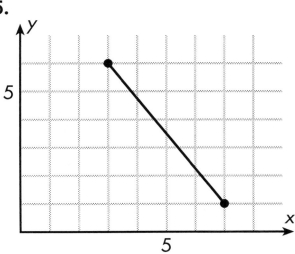

6.

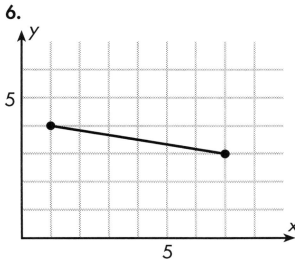

Exercise 14.

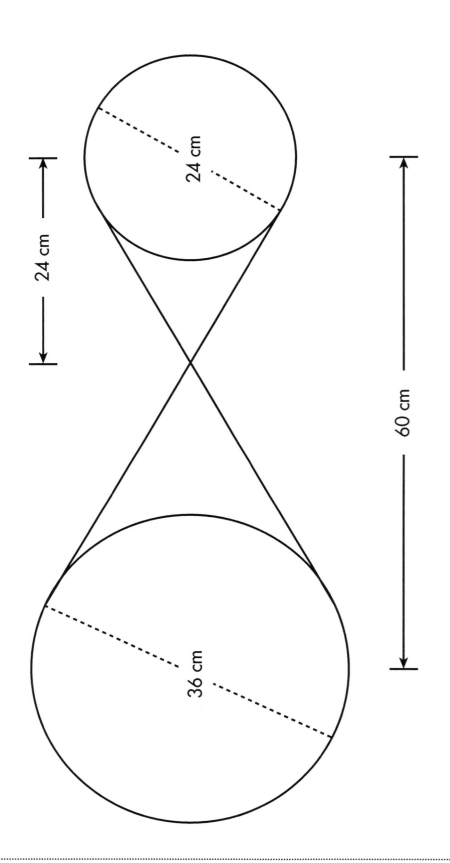

Exercise 27.

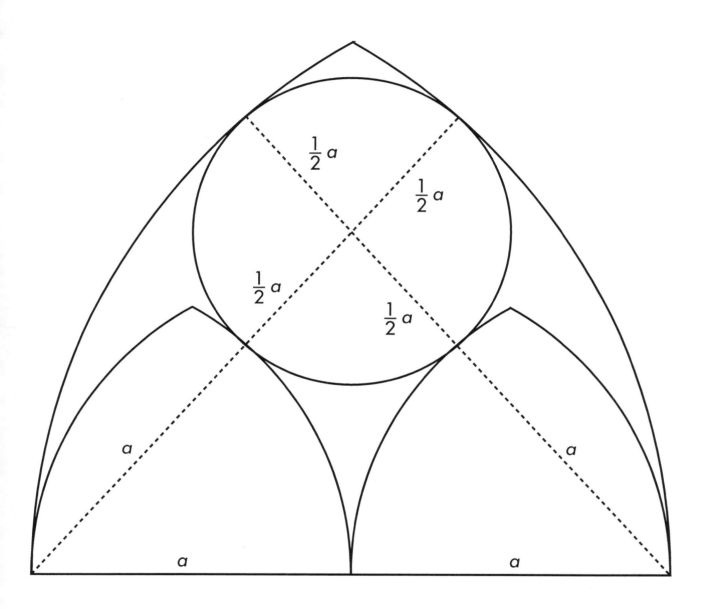

Exercises 1–9.

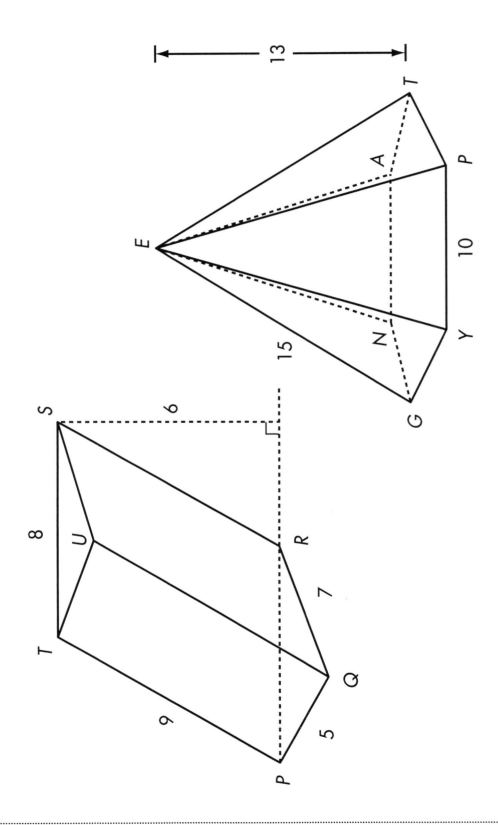

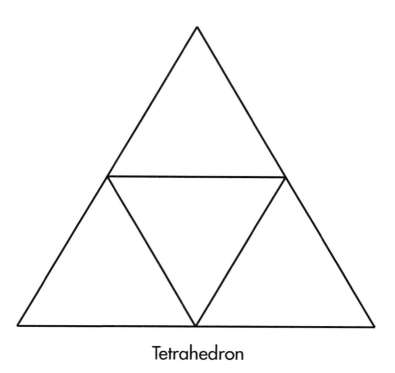

Tetrahedron

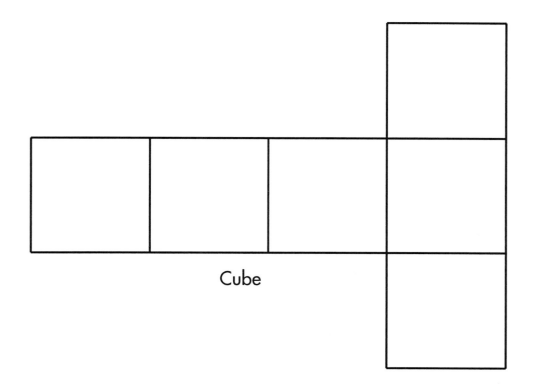

Cube

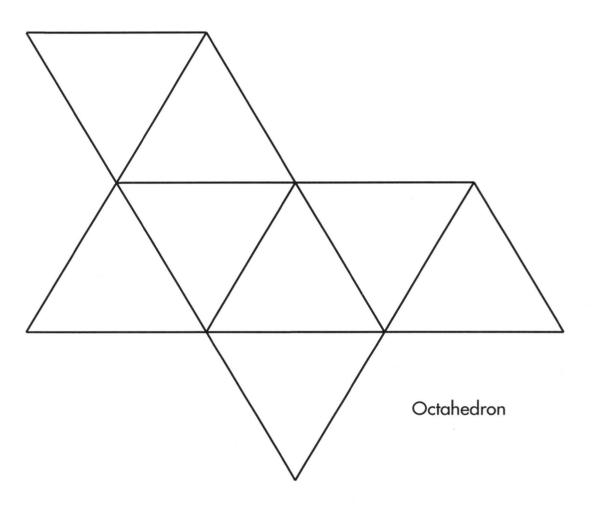

Octahedron

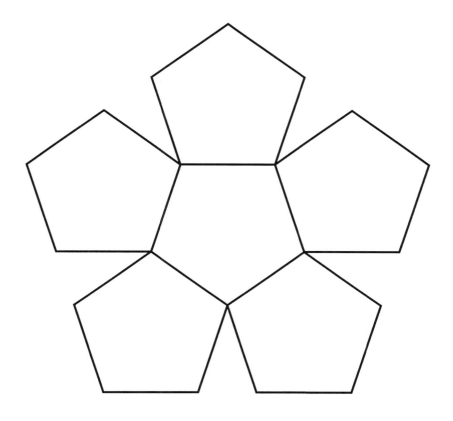

Dodecahedron

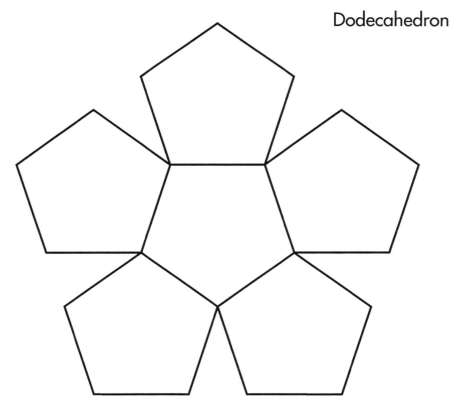

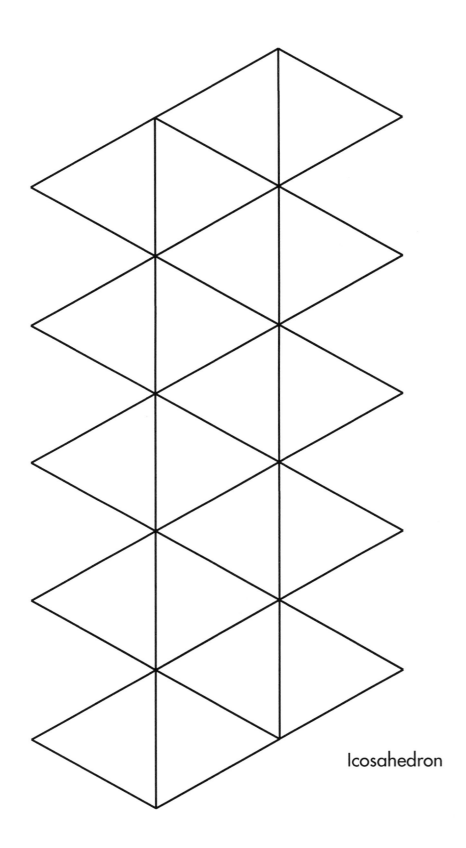

Icosahedron

Discovering Geometry Teacher's Resource Book

Investigation 11.3.

1.

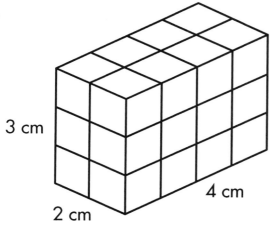

3 cm

2 cm

4 cm

2.

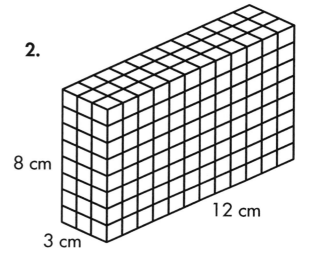

8 cm

3 cm

12 cm

3.

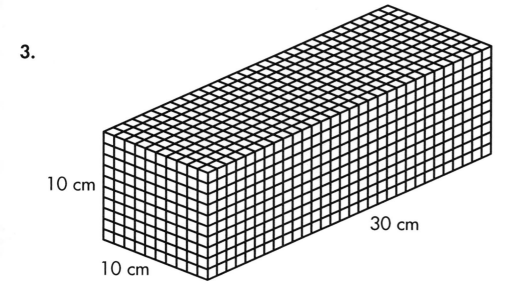

10 cm

10 cm

30 cm

Investigation 12.2.1.*

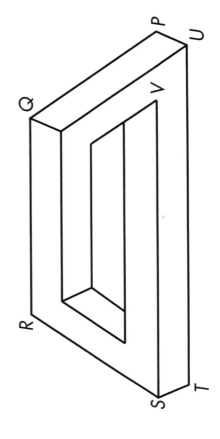

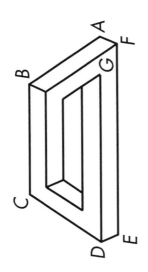

Project: The Shadow Knows

Table for Measurements by Shadow Method

Name of object to be measured	Height of observer	Shadow length of observer	Shadow length of object	Calculated height of object
1.				
2.				

Table for Measurements by Mirror Method

Name of object to be measured	Height of observer's eye	Distance from observer to mirror	Distance from object to mirror	Calculated height of object
1.				
2.				

Exercise 23.

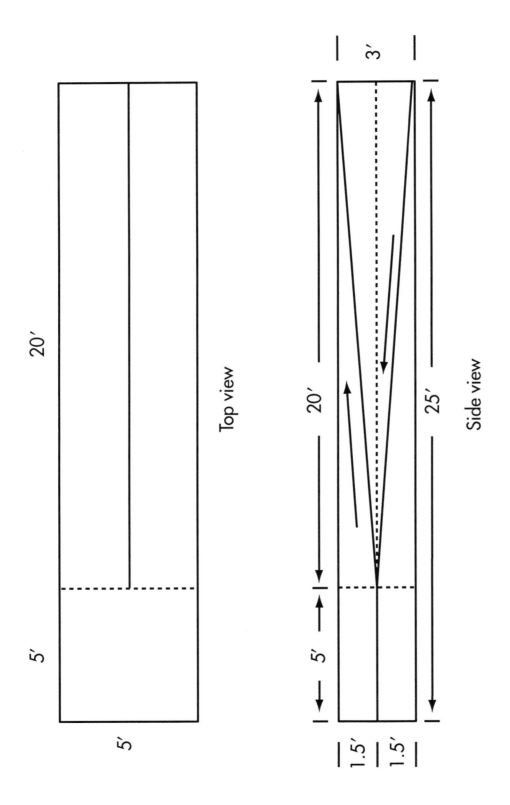

Top view

20'

5'

5'

Side view

3'

20'

25'

5'

1.5'   1.5'

Exercises 1 and 2.

1.

Premises:	Proof:	
P	**1.** $P \rightarrow Q$	**1.**
$P \rightarrow Q$	**2.** $Q \rightarrow R$	**2.**
$Q \rightarrow R$	**3.** $P \rightarrow R$	**3.***
$R \rightarrow S$	**4.** $R \rightarrow S$	**4.**
Conclusion:	**5.** $P \rightarrow S$	**5.**
S	**6.** P	**6.**
	7. $\therefore S$	**7.**

2.

Premises:	Proof:	
$P \rightarrow Q$	**1.** $Q \rightarrow \sim R$	**1.**
$Q \rightarrow \sim R$	**2.** R	**2.**
R	**3.** $\sim Q$	**3.**
Conclusion:	**4.** $P \rightarrow Q$	**4.**
$\sim P$	**5.** $\therefore \sim P$	**5.**

Lesson 14.7/Page 702

Exercises 3 and 4.

3.*

Premises:

$P \rightarrow R$

$T \rightarrow S$

$\sim T \rightarrow P$

$\sim S$

Conclusion:

R

Proof:

1. $T \rightarrow S$

2. $\sim S$

3. $\sim T$

4. $\sim T \rightarrow P$

5. P

6.

7.

1.

2.

3.

4.

5.*

6.

7.

4.*

Premises:

$P \rightarrow R$

$T \rightarrow S$

$\sim T \rightarrow P$

$\sim S$

Conclusion:

R

Proof:

1. $T \rightarrow S$

2. $\sim S \rightarrow \sim T$

3. $\sim T \rightarrow P$

4. $\sim S \rightarrow P$

5. $P \rightarrow R$

6.

7.

8.

1.

2.*

3.

4.

5.

6.

7.

8.

Exercises 1 and 2.

1.*

Premises:	$P \rightarrow R$	**Proof:**	
	$S \rightarrow \sim R$	**1.** $\sim Q$	**1.**
	$\sim P \rightarrow Q$	**2.** $\sim P \rightarrow Q$	**2.**
Conclusion:	$\sim Q \rightarrow \sim S$	**3.** P	**3.** From lines 1 and 2, using
		4. $P \rightarrow R$	**4.**
		5. R	**5.** From lines 3 and 4, using
		6. $S \rightarrow \sim R$	**6.**
		7. $\sim S$	**7.*** From lines 5 and 6, using

Assuming ___ is true, the truth of ___ is established.

$\therefore \sim Q \rightarrow \sim S$

2.

Premises:	$\sim R \rightarrow \sim Q$	**Proof:**	
	$T \rightarrow \sim R$	**1.** S	**1.**
	$S \rightarrow T$	**2.** $S \rightarrow T$	**2.**
Conclusion:	$S \rightarrow \sim Q$	**3.** T	**3.** From lines 1 and 2, using
		4. $T \rightarrow \sim R$	**4.**
		5. $\sim R$	**5.** From lines 3 and 4, using
		6. $\sim R \rightarrow \sim Q$	**6.**
		7. $\sim Q$	**7.** From lines 5 and 6, using

Assuming S is true, the truth of $\sim Q$ is established.

$\therefore$ _____

Lesson 14.9/Page 710　　　　　　　　　　　　　T

Exercises 4–5.

4.

Premises:　$P \to Q$　　　　**Proof:**

　　　　　　　$R \to P$　　　　**1.** R　　　　**1.** Assume the opposite of the

　　　　　　　$\sim Q$　　　　　**2.** $R \to P$　**2.**

Conclusion:　$\sim R$　　　　**3.** P　　　　**3.** From lines 1 and 2, using

　　　　　　　　　　　　　　4. $P \to Q$　**4.**

　　　　　　　　　　　　　　5. Q　　　　**5.** From lines ___ and ___, using MP

　　　　　　　　　　　　　　6. $\sim Q$　　　**6.**

　　　　　　　　　　　　　　But lines 5 and 6 contradict each other.

　　　　　　　　　　　　　　Therefore, R, the assumption, is false. $\therefore \sim R$

5.*

Premises:　$P \to (Q \to R)$　**Proof:**

　　　　　　　$Q \to \sim R$　　　**1.** P　　　　**1.** Assume the ___ of the ___

　　　　　　　Q　　　　　　**2.** $P \to (Q \to R)$　**2.**

Conclusion:　$\sim P$　　　　**3.** $Q \to R$　**3.***

　　　　　　　　　　　　　　4. Q　　　　**4.**

　　　　　　　　　　　　　　5. R　　　　**5.**

　　　　　　　　　　　　　　6.　　　　　**6.**

　　　　　　　　　　　　　　7.　　　　　**7.** From lines ___ and ___, using MP

　　　　　　　　　　　　　　But lines 6 and 7 contradict each other.

　　　　　　　　　　　　　　Therefore, P, the assumption is false. $\therefore \sim P$

Discovering Geometry Teacher's Resource Book
© 1997 by Key Curriculum Press. All rights reserved.

Exercise 6.

6.

Premises:	$(P \rightarrow S) \rightarrow \sim R$	**Proof:**	
	$\sim Q \rightarrow R$	1. $\sim S \rightarrow \sim P$	1. Assume the ___ of the ___
	$\sim R$	2.	2.
Conclusion:	$\sim(\sim S \rightarrow \sim P)$	3.	3.
		4.	4.
		5.	5.
		6.	6.
		7.	7.

But lines 6 and 7 contradict each other.

Therefore, $\sim S \rightarrow \sim P$, the assumption is false.

$\therefore \sim(\sim S \rightarrow \sim P)$

Exercises 12 and 13.

12.

Equation:	$7x - 22 = 4(x + 2)$	
Solution:	$7x - 22 = 4(x + 2)$	Given
	$7x - 22 = 4x + 8$	_____ property
	$3x - 22 = 8$	_____ property of equality
	$3x = 30$	_____ property of equality
	$x = 10$	_____ property of equality

13.

Equation:	$\dfrac{5(x - 12)}{4} = 3(2x - 7)$	
Solution:	$\dfrac{5(x - 12)}{4} = 3(2x - 7)$	Given
	$5(x - 12) = 12(2x - 7)$	_____ property of equality
	$5x - 60 = 24x - 84$	_____ property
	$5x = 24x - 24$	_____ property of equality
	$-19x = -24$	_____ property of equality
	$x = \dfrac{24}{19}$	_____ property of equality

Exercises 11 and 12.

11.

   Given: $\overline{AC} \cong \overline{BD}$; $\overline{AD} \cong \overline{BC}$

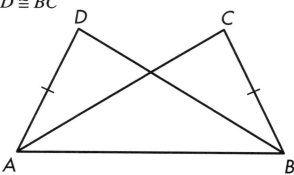

Statement:	Reason:
1. $\overline{AC} \cong \overline{BD}$	**1.**
$\overline{AD} \cong \overline{BC}$	
2. $\overline{AB} \cong \overline{AB}$	**2.**
3. $\triangle ABC \cong \triangle BAD$	**3.**
4. $\angle D \cong \angle C$	**4.**

12.*

   Given: $\overline{AB} \parallel \overline{CD}$

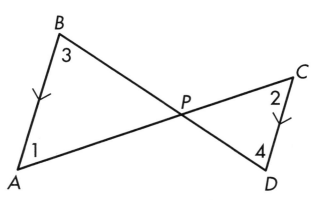

Statement:	Reason:
1. $\overline{AB} \parallel \overline{CD}$	**1.**
2. $\angle 1 \cong \angle 1$	**2.**
$\angle 3 \cong \angle 4$	

Theorem List

Theorem: The angle bisector of the vertex angle of an isosceles triangle is also a median to the base.

Theorem: The median from the vertex angle of an isosceles triangle bisects the vertex angle.

You are to start at square 1 and move to square 100. You can move to an adjacent square, horizontally, vertically, or diagonally, whenever you can add, subtract, multiply, or divide the number in the square you occupy by 2 or 5 to get the number in the adjacent square.

1	5	10	20	30
2	3	22	6	28
4	27	8	14	19
20	17	11	55	95
18	9	50	57	100

Introduction to the Extra Practice Worksheets

This section contains extra practice worksheets designed to accompany selected lessons in the *Discovering Geometry* student text. The worksheets contain supplemental exercises for some of the curriculum's core lessons. The exercises are similar to those found in the student text and can be used to assist students having difficulty with a particular concept, for a midchapter review, or as extra credit material. You can also use the worksheets as models for worksheets you develop yourself to accommodate the particular needs of your students.

The worksheets were developed by Ralph Bothe and Judy Hicks under the guidance of Michael Serra. Answers to the worksheet exercises can be found at the end of this section.

Chapter 1

Name _____ Period _____ Date _____

Lesson 1.2

Draw the next shape in each picture pattern.

1.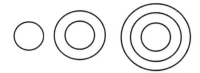

2.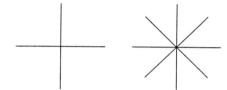

3.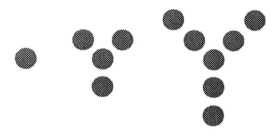

Lesson 1.4

Find the *n*th term and the 20th term in each sequence.

4.

1	2	3	4	5	6	. . .	n	. . .	20
–2	1	4	7	10	13	. . .		. . .	

5.

1	2	3	4	5	6	. . .	n	. . .	20
4	6	8	10	12	14	. . .		. . .	

6.

1	2	3	4	5	6	. . .	n	. . .	20
2	7	12	17	22	27	. . .		. . .	

7.

1	2	3	4	5	6	. . .	n	. . .	20
5	4	3	2	1	0	. . .		. . .	

Chapter 1

Practice 2

Name _____ Period _____ Date _____

Lesson 1.5

Find the *n*th term and the 20th term in each sequence.

1.

1	2	3	4	5	6	. . .	n	. . .	20
4	15	32	55	84	119	. . .		. . .	

2.

1	2	3	4	5	6	. . .	n	. . .	20
–6	7	24	45	70	99	. . .		. . .	

3.

1	2	3	4	5	6	. . .	n	. . .	20
3	20	49	90	143	208	. . .		. . .	

4.

1	2	3	4	5	6	. . .	n	. . .	20
5	35	81	143	221	315	. . .		. . .	

5.

1	2	3	4	5	6	. . .	n	. . .	20
2	30	88	176	294	442	. . .		. . .	

6.

1	2	3	4	5	6	. . .	n	. . .	20
–6	5	40	99	182	289	. . .		. . .	

7.

1	2	3	4	5	6	. . .	n	. . .	20
3	3	35	99	195	323	. . .		. . .	

Name _____ **Period** _____ **Date** _____

8.

1	2	3	4	5	6	. . .	n	. . .	20
7	70	169	304	475	682	. . .		. . .	

9.

1	2	3	4	5	6	. . .	n	. . .	20
0	0	1	3	6	10	. . .		. . .	

10.

1	2	3	4	5	6	. . .	n	. . .	20
−1	0	2	5	9	14	. . .		. . .	

11.

1	2	3	4	5	6	. . .	n	. . .	20
−3	0	4	9	15	22	. . .		. . .	

12.

1	2	3	4	5	6	. . .	n	. . .	20
−5	−3	0	4	9	15	. . .		. . .	

13.

1	2	3	4	5	6	. . .	n	. . .	20
6	28	65	117	184	266	. . .		. . .	

14.

1	2	3	4	5	6	. . .	n	. . .	20
−12	−11	−7	0	10	23	. . .		. . .	

15.

1	2	3	4	5	6	. . .	n	. . .	20
−15	−7	4	18	35	55	. . .		. . .	

Name _____ Period _____ Date _____

In Exercises 1–24, match the symbol or the term on the left with one of the figures on the right.

1. Right triangle _____
2. Rhombus _____
3. Base angles _____
4. $\overleftrightarrow{DA}$ _____
5. Regular octagon _____
6. Linear pair _____
7. Parallelogram _____
8. Equilateral hexagon _____
9. $\overrightarrow{AB}$ _____
10. Median _____
11. Coplanar points _____
12. Kite _____
13. Obtuse angle _____
14. Diagonal of a polygon _____
15. $\overline{FC}$ _____
16. Equiangular pentagon _____
17. Isosceles triangle _____
18. $\angle BAC$ _____
19. Scalene triangle _____
20. Altitude _____
21. Supplementary angles _____
22. Trapezoid _____
23. Angle bisector _____
24. Acute angle _____

a.

b.

c.
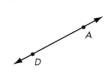

d.

e.

f.
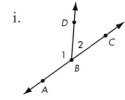

g.
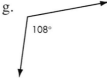

h.
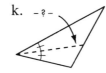

i.
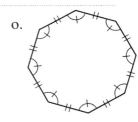

j.
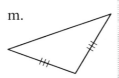

k.
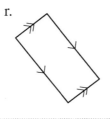

l.
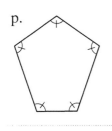

m.
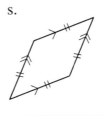

n.

o.
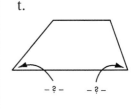

p.
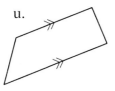

q.
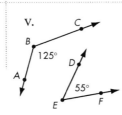

r.
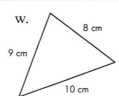

s.
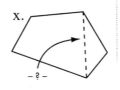

t.

u.

v.

w.

x.

Name _____ Period _____ Date _____

In Exercises 1–20, sketch an example of each term.

1. Collinear points	**2.** $\overleftrightarrow{AB}$	**3.** $\overline{AB}$	**4.** $\overrightarrow{AB}$
5. $\angle ABC$	**6.** Acute angle	**7.** $\overleftrightarrow{AB} \perp \overline{CD}$	**8.** $\overrightarrow{AB}$ // $\overline{CD}$
9. Midpoint A	**10.** Angle bisector	**11.** Obtuse triangle	**12.** Complementary angles
13. Vertical angles	**14.** Altitude of a triangle	**15.** Diagonal of a polygon	**16.** Rhombus
17. Parallelogram	**18.** Equilateral hexagon	**19.** Right triangle	**20.** Scalene triangle

Name _____ Period _____ Date _____

In Exercises 1–24, name each
sketched figure.

1. _____

2. _____

3. _____

4. _____

5. _____

6. _____

7. _____

8. _____

9. _____

10. _____

11. _____

12. _____

13. _____

14. _____

15. _____

16. _____

17. _____

18. _____

19. _____

20. _____

21. _____

22. _____

23. _____

24. _____

1.
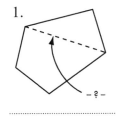

2.

3.
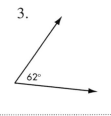

4.
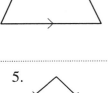

5.
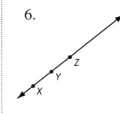

6.
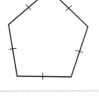

7.
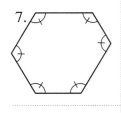

8.
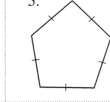

9.

10.
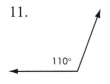

11.
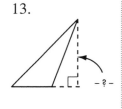

12.
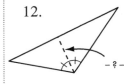

13.
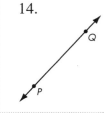

14.
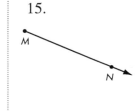

15.
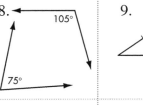

16.
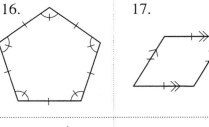

17.
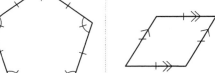

18.
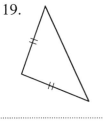

19.
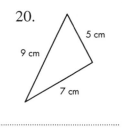

20.

21.
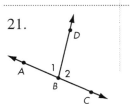

22.

23.

24.
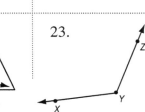

Chapter 3

Name _____ Period _____ Date _____

In Exercises 1–12, match each geometric construction with one of the figures below:

1. Construction of an angle bisector _____
2. Construction of a perpendicular from a point to a line _____
3. Construction of an orthocenter _____
4. Construction of an altitude in a triangle _____
5. Construction of a perpendicular through a point on a line _____
6. Construction of a perpendicular bisector _____
7. Construction of a line parallel to a given line through a given point not on the line _____
8. Construction of an incenter _____
9. Construction of a centroid _____
10. Construction of an equilateral triangle _____
11. Construction of a circumcenter _____
12. Construction of an inscribed circle _____

a.
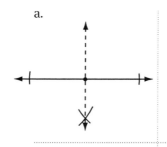

b.
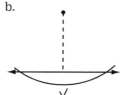

c.
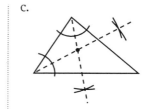

d.
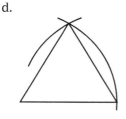

e.
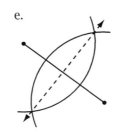

f.
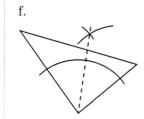

g.
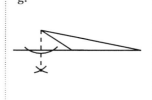

h.
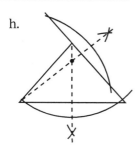

i.
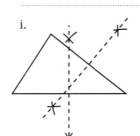

j.
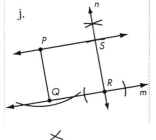

k.
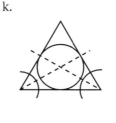

l.
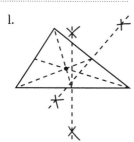

Chapter 4

Practice 1

Name _____ Period _____ Date _____

Lessons 4.4 and 4.5

In Exercises 1–10, determine whether each figure or set of coordinates forms a right triangle, a trapezoid, a parallelogram, a rectangle, or just an ordinary quadrilateral. Explain how you know.

1.

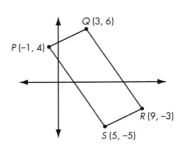

2.

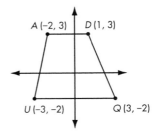

3.

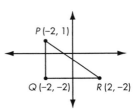

4.

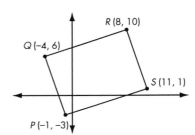

5.

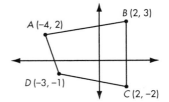

Name _____ **Period** _____ **Date** _____

6. $T(2, 3)$, $U(-4, 3)$, $V(-4, -3)$

7. $A(3, 1)$, $B(10, 1)$, $C(7, 9)$, $D(5, 9)$

8. $E(2, 1)$, $F(3, 4)$, $G(7, 2)$, $H(6, -1)$

9. $E(0, -3)$, $F(-3, 0)$, $G(0, 3)$, $H(3, 0)$

10. $D(-7, 3)$, $E(-2, 3)$, $F(1, 7)$, $G(-4, 7)$

In Exercises 11–20, graph each linear equation.

11. $y = 2x - 3$ **12.** $y = x + 2$

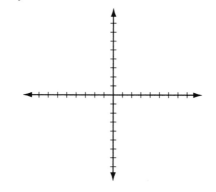
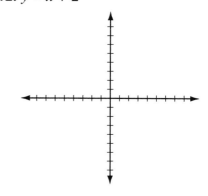

Name _____ Period _____ Date _____

13. $2x - y = 3$

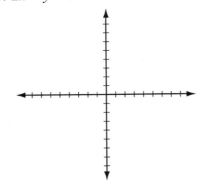

14. $y = -3x + 2$

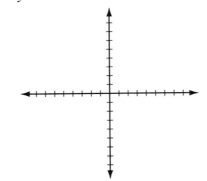

15. $y = 5$

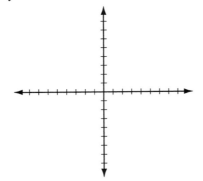

16. $3x - 6y = 12$

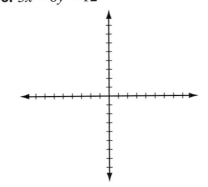

17. $2x + y = 3$

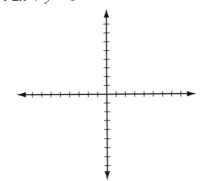

18. $y + 4x = 2$

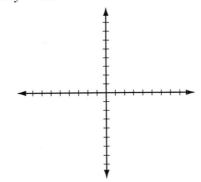

19. $2x - y = 4$

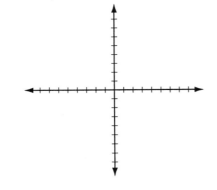

20. $x + y = 8$

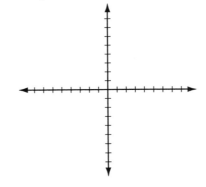

Name _____ **Period** _____ **Date** _____

For each line, determine the equation in slope-intercept form.

21.

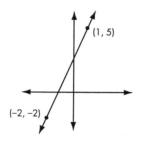

_____

22.

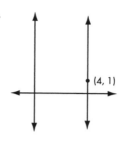

_____

23.

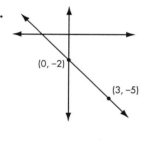

_____

24.

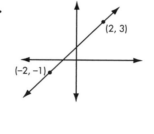

_____

25.

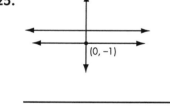

_____

26.

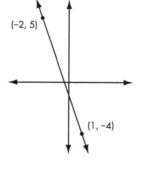

_____

27.

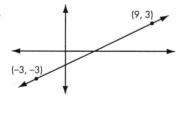

_____

28.

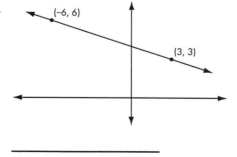

_____

Chapter 4

Name _____ **Period** _____ **Date** _____

Lesson 4.6

In Exercises 1–10, solve each system of equations graphically and algebraically.

1. $x + y = 3$
    $x - y = 1$
    (____ , ____)

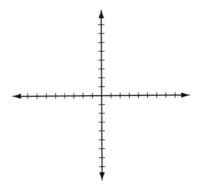

2. $y = 3 + x$
    $x + y = 5$
    (____ , ____)

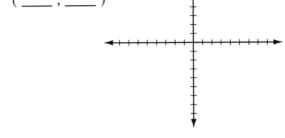

3. $2x - y = 3$
    $3x + 2y = 22$
    (____ , ____)

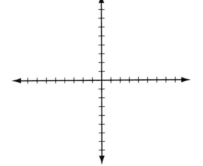

4. $x = 4$
    $y = 3x - 5$
    (____ , ____)

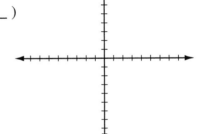

5. $y = 2x + 1$
    $y = 4x + 7$
    (____ , ____)

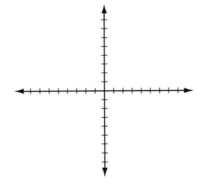

6. $y = 2x$
    $x + y = 3$
    (____ , ____)

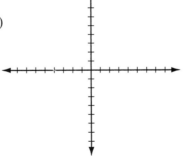

7. $x + y = 3$
$3x - 5y = 17$
(_____ , _____)

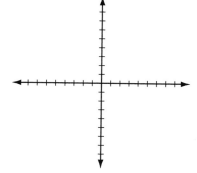

8. $x + y = 7$
$x - y = 9$
(_____ , _____)

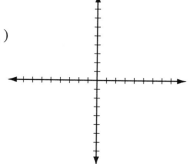

9. $2x + 3y = -1$
$3x + 5y = -2$
(_____ , _____)

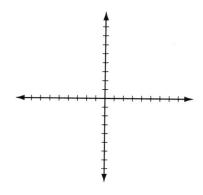

10. $4x - 3y = -1$
$x + 1 = y$
(_____ , _____)

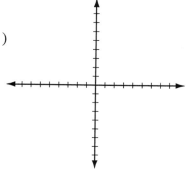

In Exercises 11–16, find the coordinates of the centroid, the circumcenter, and the orthocenter of each triangle.

11. $A(0, 7)$, $B(-6, 1)$, $C(6, -5)$
Centroid: (_____ , _____)
Circumcenter: (_____ , _____)
Orthocenter: (_____ , _____)

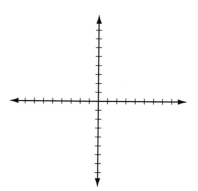

12. $A(1, 7)$, $B(-3, 2)$, $C(7, -6)$
Centroid: (_____ , _____)
Circumcenter: (_____ , _____)
Orthocenter: (_____ , _____)

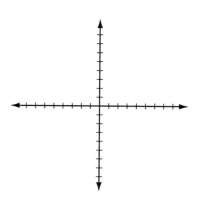

Name _____ Period _____ Date _____

13. $A(-2, 5)$, $B(6, 1)$, $C(-2, -5)$
Centroid: (_____ , _____)
Circumcenter: (_____ , _____)
Orthocenter: (_____ , _____)

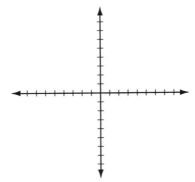

14. $R(0, 10)$, $S(-5, 0)$, $T(5, 5)$
Centroid: (_____ , _____)
Circumcenter: (_____ , _____)
Orthocenter: (_____ , _____)

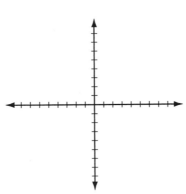

15. $D(0, 12)$, $E(-2, 10)$, $F(4, 6)$
Centroid: (_____ , _____)
Circumcenter: (_____ , _____)
Orthocenter: (_____ , _____)

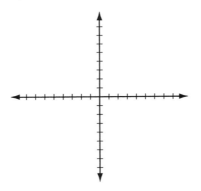

16. $A(4, 1)$, $B(-3, -1)$, $C(4, -3)$
Centroid: (_____ , _____)
Circumcenter: (_____ , _____)
Orthocenter: (_____ , _____)

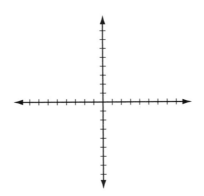

Name _____ Period _____ Date _____

Lesson 5.3

For each set of lengths, determine whether it is possible to draw a triangle with sides of the given measures.

1. 3 cm, 3 cm, 3 cm _____

2. 2 m, 3 m, 4 m _____

3. 1 ft, 2 ft, 3 ft _____

4. 8.9 cm, 9.3 cm, 18.3 cm _____

5. 16.5 in., 20.5 in., 38.6 in. _____

6. 19 ft, 19 ft, 0.5 ft _____

In Exercises 7–11, the letter on each side of each triangle indicates that side's measure and the letter in the interior of an angle indicates that angle's measure. Use you new conjectures to arrange the letters' values in order from least to greatest.

7.
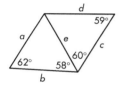

_____

8.
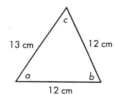

_____

9.
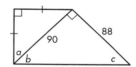

_____

10.
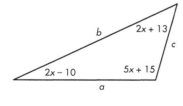

_____

11.
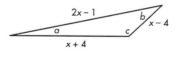

_____

In Exercises 12 and 13, name each triangle's longest side and angle with least measure.

12.
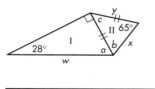

_____

_____

13.
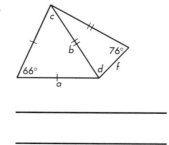

_____

_____

Chapter 5

Practice 2

Name _____ Period _____ Date _____

Lesson 5.4

1. What conjecture tells you that $\triangle AND$ is congruent to $\triangle DYA$?

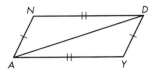

_____

2. What conjecture tells you that $\triangle PTA$ is congruent to $\triangle PTR$?

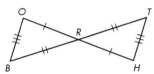

_____

3. What conjecture tells you that $\triangle ROB$ is congruent to $\triangle RHT$?

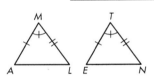

_____

From the information given, complete each statement. If the triangles cannot be shown to be congruent from the information given, write "Cannot be determined" and redraw the figures to show that the triangles are clearly not congruent. Do not assume that segments or angles are congruent just because they appear to be congruent.

4. $\triangle MAL \cong$ _____

5. $\triangle HED \cong$ _____

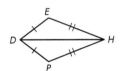

6. $\triangle ABH \cong$ _____

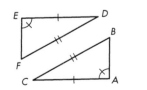

7. $ABCD$ is a rhombus.
   $\triangle ABD \cong$ _____

8. $\triangle XYZ \cong$ _____

9. $\triangle ACB \cong$ _____

10. $\overline{AB} \perp \overline{BC}$, $\overline{DC} \perp \overline{CB}$
    $\triangle ABC \cong$ _____

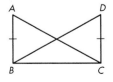

11. $\overline{NA}$ bisects $\overline{RI}$, $\overline{RN} \cong \overline{IN}$
    $\triangle RAN \cong$ _____

12. $\triangle AED \cong$ _____

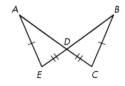

Chapter 5

Practice 2

Name _____ Period _____ Date _____

Lesson 5.5

13. What conjecture tells you that △ABC is congruent to △MNO? _____

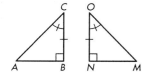

14. What conjecture tells you that △DEF is congruent to △MNO? _____

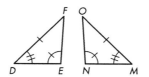

15. What conjecture tells you that △XZY is congruent to △XZW? _____

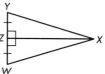

From the information given, complete each statement. If the triangles cannot be shown to be congruent from the information given, write "Cannot be determined" and redraw the figures to show that the triangles are clearly not congruent. Do not assume that segments or angles are congruent just because they appear to be congruent.

16. ROWB is a rectangle.
△RBW ≅ _____

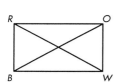

17. $\overline{AC} \perp \overline{NP}$, $\overline{NR} \perp \overline{AP}$
△ACN ≅ _____

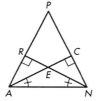

18. $\overline{MB} \cong \overline{ME}$, ∠MBL ≅ ∠MEA
△MBL ≅ _____

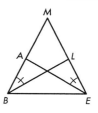

19. △ABC ≅ _____

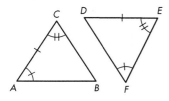

20. $\overline{RB} \cong \overline{NT}$, $\overline{AR} \cong \overline{EN}$,
∠ART ≅ ∠ENB
△ART ≅ _____

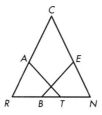

21. $\overline{GR} \cong \overline{GE}$, ∠EQG ≅ ∠RPG,
∠RGP ≅ ∠EGQ
△RGP ≅ _____

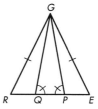

22. ∠1 ≅ ∠2, $\overline{PR} \cong \overline{SU}$,
$\overline{RQ} \cong \overline{UT}$
△PRQ ≅ _____

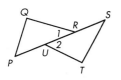

23. ABCD is a parallelogram. ∠BEA and ∠DFC are right angles.
△BEA ≅ _____

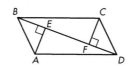

24. EFGH is a parallelogram.
$\overline{GQ} \cong \overline{EQ}$
△EQL ≅ _____

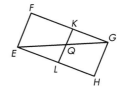

Chapter 6   Practice 1

Name _____ Period _____ Date _____

Lesson 6.4

In Exercises 1–6, calculate each missing measure.

1. $m\angle E =$ _____

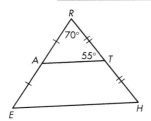

2. $EF =$ _____

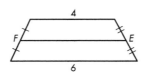

3. $x =$ _____

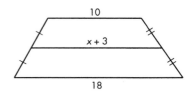

4. $x =$ _____

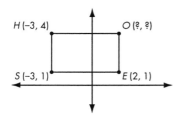

5. Perimeter of $\triangle NTM =$

_____

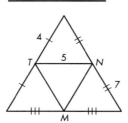

6. Perimeter of $\triangle TOP =$

_____

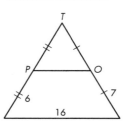

7. *SHOE* is a rectangle. What are the coordinates of point O? _____

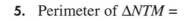

8. *TABL* is a trapezoid. What are the coordinates of point L? _____

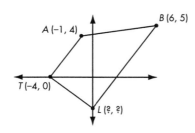

9. *CHAI* is a parallelogram. What are the coordinates of point A? _____

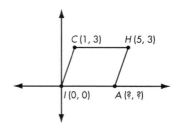

10. RULE is a kite. What are the coordinates of point *E*? _____

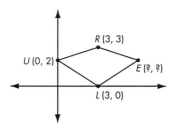

11. *PLAN* is a kite. What are the coordinates of point *N*?

_____

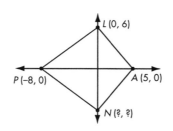

12. *UOVW* is an isosceles trapezoid. What are the coordinates of point *W*?

_____

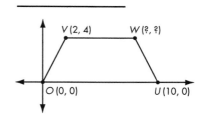

13. Calculate the measure of each lettered angle.

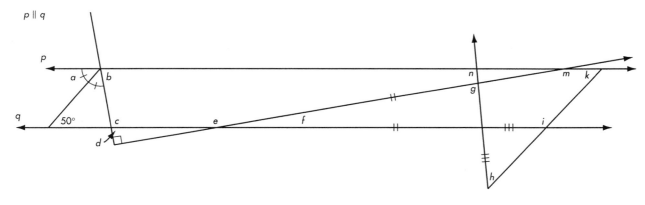

$a =$ _____ $e =$ _____ $i =$ _____

$b =$ _____ $f =$ _____ $k =$ _____

$c =$ _____ $g =$ _____ $m =$ _____

$d =$ _____ $h =$ _____ $n =$ _____

Name _____ Period _____ Date _____

Lesson 7.4

Use the conjectures from Lesson 7.4 to solve Exercises 1–8.

1. $m\widehat{XM} = 80°$
  $m\angle XNM =$ _____
  $m\widehat{XN} =$ _____
  $m\widehat{MN} =$ _____

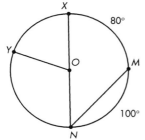

2. $\overline{AB}$ is a tangent.
  $x =$ _____
  $y =$ _____
  $z =$ _____

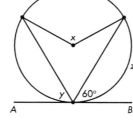
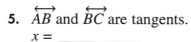

3. $a =$ _____
  $b =$ _____

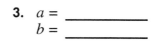
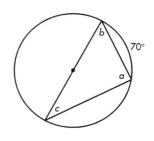

4. $a =$ _____
  $b =$ _____
  $c =$ _____

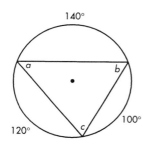

5. $\overleftrightarrow{AB}$ and $\overleftrightarrow{BC}$ are tangents.
  $x =$ _____

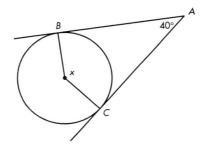

6. $\overline{AD}$ is a tangent. $\overline{AC}$ is a diameter.
  $m\angle A =$ _____
  $m\,\widehat{AB} =$ _____
  $m\angle C =$ _____
  $m\,\widehat{CB} =$ _____

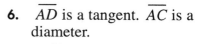
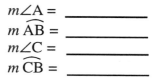
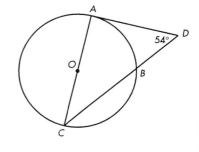

7. $m\widehat{AD} =$ _____
  $m\angle D =$ _____
  $m\,\widehat{AB} =$ _____
  $m\,\widehat{DAB} =$ _____

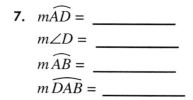
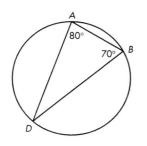

8. $m\angle ABC =$ _____
  $m\widehat{AD} =$ _____
  $m\widehat{DC} =$ _____
  $m\widehat{ADC} =$ _____
  $m\widehat{ACD} =$ _____

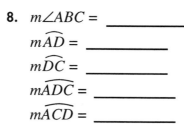
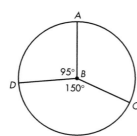

Name _____ **Period** _____ **Date** _____

9. Find the lettered angle measures and arc measures.

$a =$ _____

$b =$ _____

$c =$ _____

$d =$ _____

$e =$ _____

$f =$ _____

$g =$ _____

$h =$ _____

$j =$ _____

$k =$ _____

$m =$ _____

$n =$ _____

$p =$ _____

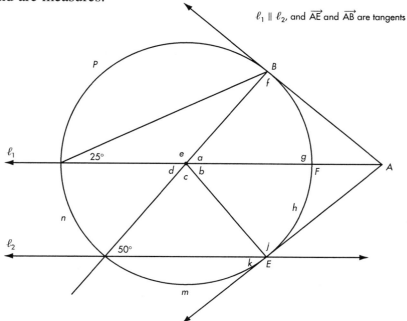

$\ell_1 \parallel \ell_2$, and $\overrightarrow{AE}$ and $\overrightarrow{AB}$ are tangents

Lesson 7.5

Solve Exercises 10–16. Do not use an approximation for π.

10. If $r = 10.5$ cm, find C.

11. If $C = 25\pi$ cm, find r.

12. If $C = 9.6\pi$ cm, find D.

13. If $D = 12$ cm, find C.

14. What is the circumference of a circle whose radius is 30 cm?

15. What is the diameter of a circle whose circumference is 24π cm?

16. A square with sides that each measure 2 cm is inscribed within a circle. Find the circumference of the circle.

Chapter 7 **Practice 2**

Name _____ Period _____ Date _____

Lesson 7.7

1. Length of $\overset{\frown}{AB}$ = _____

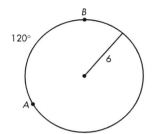

2. The circumference is 24π, and $m\overset{\frown}{CD} = 60°$.
   Length of $\overset{\frown}{CD}$ = _____

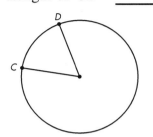

3. The length of $\overset{\frown}{EF}$ is 5π.
   Radius = _____

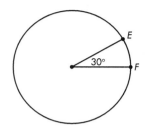

4. Length of $\overset{\frown}{XY}$ = _____

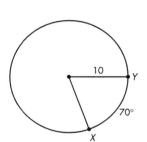

5. The radius is 20.
   Length of $\overset{\frown}{AB}$ = _____

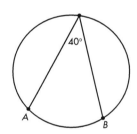

6. The circumference is 25π.
   Length of $\overset{\frown}{AB}$ = _____

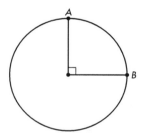

7. The diameter is 40.
   Length of $\overset{\frown}{AC}$ = _____

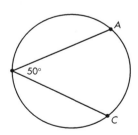

8. The length of $\overset{\frown}{XY}$ is 14π.
   Diameter = _____

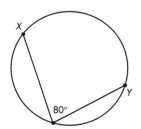

9. Length of $\overset{\frown}{AB}$ = _____

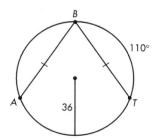

10. A circle has an arc whose measure is 80° and whose length is 88π. What is the diameter of the circle? _____

144/Extra Practice Worksheets

Discovering Geometry Teacher's Resource Book
© 1997 by Key Curriculum Press. All rights reserved.

Chapter 9

Practice 1

Lesson 9.1

1. Judy is laying tile on her kitchen counter. The counter is rectangular and measures 3 feet by 5 feet. The tiles are square and measure 3 inches on each side. How many tiles does Judy need to cover the counter?

2. Dana buys a piece of carpet that measures 20 square yards. Will she be able to completely carpet a rectangular room that measures 12.5 feet by 16.5 feet? Explain why or why not.

Lesson 9.2

Use your area conjectures to solve Exercises 3–6. Express each answer accurate to the nearest tenth.

3. $A = 60$ sq. in.
    $h = $ _____

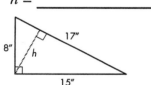

4. The figure is a trapezoid. $A = 42$ cm^2
    $h = $ _____

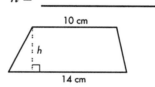

5. The figure is a parallelogram.
    $h = $ _____

6. $A = 66$ cm^2
    $x = $ _____

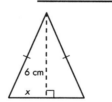

Lesson 9.3

7. Jason wants to paint the four walls and the ceiling of his room. The room is rectangular and measures 12 feet by 14 feet. The ceiling is 8 feet high. A quart of paint will cover 100 square feet, and a gallon will cover 400 square feet. Assuming Jason will paint the doors and that there are no windows in the room, how much paint should he buy? Explain your answer.

8. Gabriella wants to put vinyl in the family room diagrammed at right. The vinyl comes in rolls that are 6′ wide and as long as needed. What is the minimum length of vinyl that Gabriella needs to complete her job? Illustrate how she could lay the vinyl. What is the minimum number of seams?

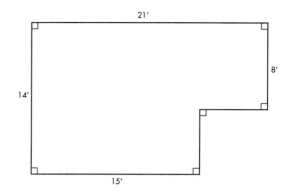

Lesson 9.5

In Exercises 9–12, state each answer in terms of π.

9. Find the circumference of a circle whose area is 36π cm².

10. Find the area of a circle whose circumference is 9π cm.

11. Find the diameter of a circle whose area is $(9/4)\pi$ cm².

12. Find the radius of a circle whose circumference is 12 cm.

Chapter 9

Name _____ **Period** _____ **Date** _____

Lesson 9.6

In Exercises 1–4, find the shaded area. The radius of each circle is *r*. If two circles are shown, *r* is the radius of the smaller and *R* is the radius of the larger. All given measurements are in centimeters. State each answer in terms of π.

1. $r = 10$
$A =$ _____

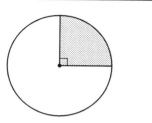

2. $r = 6$
$A =$ _____

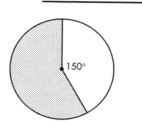

3. $A =$ _____

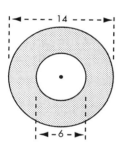

4. $R = 16$
$r = 6$
$A =$ _____

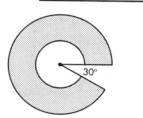

Lessons 9.7 and 9.8

5. Find the surface area of a right rectangular solid whose edges measure 8 in., 14 in., and 16 in.

6. Find the surface area of a right cylinder whose base circumference is 8π cm and whose height is 18 cm.

7. Find the surface area of a right cone whose base radius is 3 ft, whose height is 4 ft, and whose slant height is 5 ft.

8. Find the total surface area of a rectangular room that measures 7 meters by 10 meters by 5 meters high. Ignore doorways and windows.

Chapter 10 — Practice 1

Name _____ Period _____ Date _____

Lesson 10.1

In Exercises 1–4, find each missing length. All measurements are in centimeters.

1. $d =$ _____   **2.** $g =$ _____   **3.** $x =$ _____   **4.** $x =$ _____

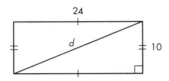
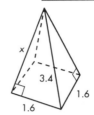
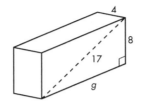
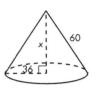

Lesson 10.2

In Exercises 5 and 6, determine whether the lengths could be the side lengths of a right triangle.

5. 80, 18, 82 _____   **6.** 0.5, 1.2, 1.4 _____

Lesson 10.3

7. If the diagonal of a rectangle measures 60″ and one side measures 48″, what is the length of the other side? _____

Lesson 10.4

In Exercises 8–10, find each missing length. All lengths are in centimeters.

8. $a =$
   $b =$ **9.** $c =$
   $d =$ **10.** $e =$
   $f =$

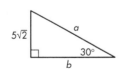
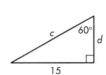

11. What are the coordinates of point A?   **12.** What are the coordinates of point B?

_____   _____

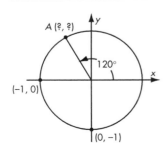
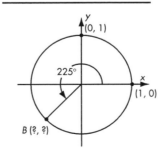

Chapter 10

Name _____ **Period** _____ **Date** _____

Lesson 10.5

1. $d =$ _____

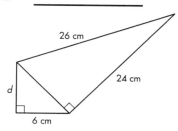

26 cm

24 cm

d

6 cm

2. What are the coordinates of point C?

_____

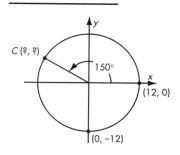

3. What are the coordinates of point D?

_____

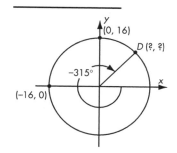

Lesson 10.7

In Exercises 4–8, use $\triangle ABC$ with vertices $A(4, 14)$, $B(10, 6)$, and $C(16, 14)$.

4. Determine whether $\triangle ABC$ is scalene, isosceles, or equilateral and find its perimeter.

5. Find the midpoints M, N, and P of $\overline{AB}$, $\overline{AC}$, and $\overline{BC}$, respectively.

6. Find the slopes of $\overline{MN}$ and $\overline{BC}$. How do they compare?

7. Find the lengths of $\overline{PN}$ and $\overline{AB}$. How do they compare?

8. Find the equation of a circle whose diameter has the endpoints $(4, -6)$ and $(-4, 0)$.

Chapter 11 Practice 1

Name _____ Period _____ Date _____

Lesson 11.3

In Exercises 1–3, find the volume of each figure. All measurements are in centimeters.

1. Right semicircular cylinder
   V = _____

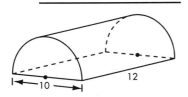

2. Trapezoidal prism
   V = _____

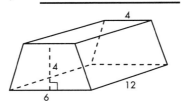

3. The quadrilaterals are rectangles.
   V = _____

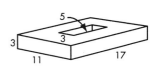

Lesson 11.4

In Exercises 4–6, find the volume of the liquid in each figure. All measurements are in centimeters.

4. Rectangular prism
   V = _____

5. Cone
   V = _____

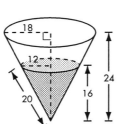

6. Rectangular prism
   V = _____

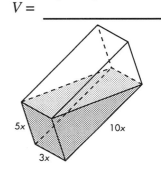

Lesson 11.5

7. Find the volume of a cube in which the diagonal of each face measures 12 cm.

8. Find the height of a cone whose volume is 500π cm³ and whose base circumference is 20π cm.

Name _____ Period _____ Date _____

Lesson 11.8

1. The surface area of a sphere is 5.76π m². Find its volume.

2. The volume of a sphere is $4\pi\sqrt{3}$ m³. Find its surface area.

Lesson 11.10

In Exercises 3–6, find the volume and the surface area of each solid. Each quadrilateral is a rectangle. If necessary, refer to Chapter 9 to review surface area. All measurements are in centimeters.

3. $V =$
$S =$

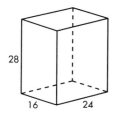

4. $V =$
$S =$

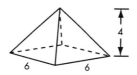

5. $V =$
$S =$

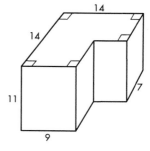

Name _____ **Period** _____ **Date** _____

6. $V =$
$S =$

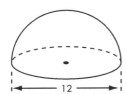

7. $V = 1.875\pi$ cm^3
$r =$

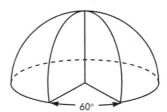

8. The volume of a cylinder is 144π cm^3. Find the diameter of the cylinder's base if its height is 16 cm.

Chapter 12   Practice 1

Name _____ Period _____ Date _____

Lesson 12.1

In Exercises 1 and 2, find the ratio of the shaded area to the area of the whole figure.

1.

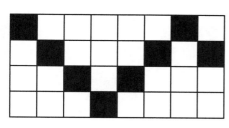

_____

2.

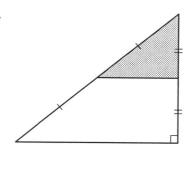

_____

3. A motor home travels 76 miles on 8 gallons of gas. How many gallons of gas are needed to travel 400 miles?

4. Blueprints for a school are drawn to the scale of 1/8″ = 1′. The dimensions of the school's new computer lab will be 20′ × 35′. What does the lab measure on the blueprints?

Lesson 12.2

In Exercises 5–8, all measurements are in centimeters.

5. *HAPIE ~ NWYRS*
   AP = _____
   EI = _____
   SR = _____
   YW = _____

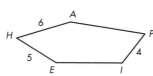

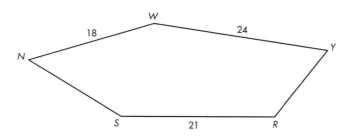

6. $\triangle TAR \sim \triangle MAC$

$MC =$ _____

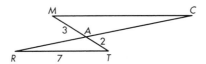

7. $\triangle TRS \sim \triangle TQP$

$TS =$ _____

$QP =$ _____

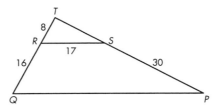

8. Are the pair of polygons similar?

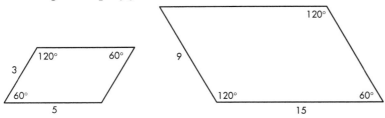

Lesson 12.4

9. At a certain time of day a 6′ man's shadow is 4′ long. At the same time of day, how tall is a tree whose shadow is 18′ long?

Name _____ Period _____ Date _____

Lesson 12.5

For Exercises 1 and 2, refer to the figure below. All measurements are in centimeters.

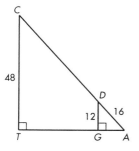

1. Explain why $\triangle CAT$ and $\triangle DAG$ are similar.

2. $CA =$

Lesson 12.6

3. The ratio of the corresponding midsegments of two similar trapezoids is 4:5. What is the ratio of their areas?

4. The ratio of the areas of two similar pentagons is 4:9. What is the ratio of their corresponding sides?

5. The corresponding heights of two similar cylinders is 2:5. What is the ratio of their volumes?

6. The ratio of the weights of two spherical balls is 27:64. What is the ratio of their radii?

7. *A*, *B*, and *C* are midpoints.

$$\frac{Area_{\triangle ABC}}{Area_{\triangle MNT}} = \underline{\hspace{3cm}}$$

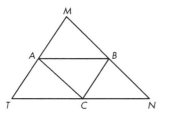

Lesson 12.7

In Exercises 8 and 9, refer to the figure below. $\overline{EB}$ // $\overline{ST}$. All measurements are in centimeters.

8. *RS* = _____

9. *EB* = _____

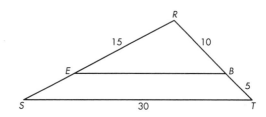

In Exercises 10 and 11, refer to the figure below. $\overline{QT}$ // $\overline{PI}$. All measurements are in centimeters.

10. *PE* = _____

11. *QT* = _____

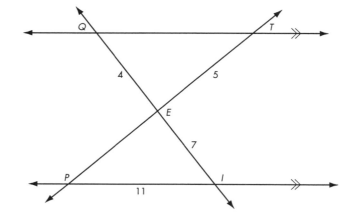

Chapter 13

Practice 1

Name _____ Period _____ Date _____

Lesson 13.1

In Exercises 1–20, use your calculator to approximate each length or angle measure. Express each answer accurate to the nearest whole unit.

1. $a \approx$ _____

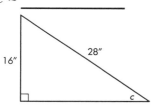

16 cm

58°

a

2. $b \approx$ _____

24 cm

b

80°

3. $c \approx$ _____

16″

28″

c

4. $d \approx$ _____

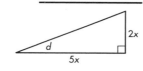

2x

d

5x

5. Perimeter $\approx$ _____

22′

6. $r = 8''$

$m \approx$ _____

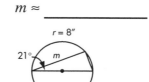

$r = 8''$

21°

m

7. The figure is a rectangle.

$e \approx$ _____

e

8 cm

15 cm

8. $x \approx$ _____

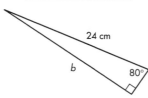

190′

50° 70°

x

Lesson 13.2

9. $a \approx$ _____

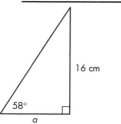

a

38°

10 cm   22 cm

10. $c \approx$ _____

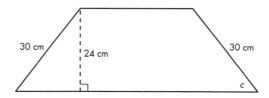

30 cm   24 cm   30 cm

c

11. $BD \approx$ _____

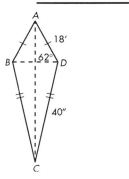

12. $a \approx$ _____

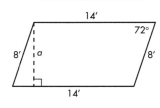

13. $\theta \approx$ _____

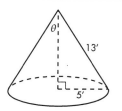

14. $\beta \approx$ _____

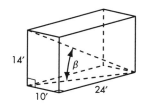

15. A ladder 7 meters long stands on level ground and rests against a wall at a point 6 meters from the ground. How far from the wall is the foot of the ladder?

16. A monument is 116 meters high and casts a shadow of 196 meters. Find the angle of elevation of the sun.

Lesson 13.5

17. A triangular lot faces two streets that meet at an angle measuring 80°. The sides of the lot facing the street are each 150 feet long. Find the perimeter of the lot.

18. The diagonals of a parallelogram are 60 in. and 70 in. and intersect at an angle measuring 64°. Find the shorter side of the parallelogram.

19. The sides of a triangle measure 8′, 10′, and 14′. Find the measure of the triangle's smallest angle.

20. Find the length of a chord that corresponds to a 54° central angle in a circle with radius 8″.

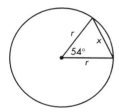

Chapter 14

Name _____ **Period** _____ **Date** _____

Lessons 14.3–14.6

Determine whether each logical argument is valid. If the argument is valid, state what logical reasoning or patterns it follows (MP, MT, LS, LC). If the argument is not valid, write "No valid conclusion."

1. $S \rightarrow \sim Y$
Y
$\therefore \sim S$

2. $\sim S$
$\sim S \rightarrow \sim Y$
$\therefore \sim Y$

3. $S \rightarrow Y$
$\therefore \sim Y \rightarrow \sim S$

4. $V \rightarrow Y$
$\sim Y$
$\therefore \sim V$

5. $\sim V$
$\sim V \rightarrow \sim Y$
$\therefore \sim Y$

6. $(U \rightarrow \sim W) \rightarrow \sim Y$
$R \rightarrow (U \rightarrow \sim W)$
$\therefore R \rightarrow \sim Y$

7. $V \rightarrow \sim (U \rightarrow \sim W)$
$U \rightarrow \sim W$
$\therefore \sim V$

8. $Q \rightarrow \sim P$
$\sim V \rightarrow \sim (P \rightarrow \sim Q)$
$\therefore V$

9. $R \rightarrow \sim S$
$\sim (Q \rightarrow \sim P) \rightarrow \sim (R \rightarrow \sim S)$
$\therefore Q \rightarrow \sim P$

10. $V \rightarrow \sim W$
$U \rightarrow W$
U
$\therefore \sim V$

11. $Q \rightarrow \sim P$
$\sim P \rightarrow \sim R$
$\sim R \rightarrow S$
$\therefore S \rightarrow \sim Q$

12. $R \rightarrow \sim S$
$\sim Q \rightarrow (\sim R \rightarrow \sim T)$
S
$\sim Q$
$\therefore \sim T$

Answers for the Extra Practice Worksheets
Chapter 1

Practice 1

1.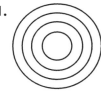

2.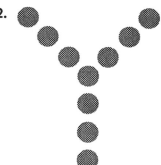

3.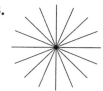

4. $3n - 5$; 55

5. $2n + 2$; 42

6. $5n - 3$; 97

7. $-n + 6$; -14

Practice 2

1. $(n + 1)(3n - 1)$; 1239

2. $(2n - 3)(n + 5)$; 925

3. $(3n - 2)(2n + 1)$; 2378

4. $(4n - 3)(2n + 3)$: 3311

5. $(5n - 4)(3n - 1)$; 5664

6. $(4n - 7)(3n - 1)$; 4307

7. $(4n - 7)(4n - 5)$; 5475

8. $(6n - 5)(3n + 4)$; 7360

9. $\frac{(n - 1)(n - 2)}{2}$; 171

10. $\frac{(n + 1)(n - 2)}{2}$; 189

11. $\frac{(n - 2)(n + 5)}{2}$; 135

12. $\frac{(n - 3)(n + 4)}{2}$; 204

13. $\frac{(5n - 2)(3n + 1)}{2}$; 549

14. $\frac{(n - 4)(3n + 5)}{2}$

15. $\frac{(n + 5)(3n - 8)}{2}$

Chapter 2

Practice 1

1. h

2. s

3. t

4. c

5. o

6. v

7. r

8. q

9. a

10. j

11. e

12. n

13. g

14. x

15. b

16. p

17. m

18. d

19. w

20. l

21. i

22. u

23. k

24. f

Practice 2

Answers will vary.

Practice 3

1. Diagonal of a polygon

2. Trapezoid

3. Acute angle

4. Right triangle

5. Equilateral pentagon

6. $\overleftrightarrow{XY}$, $\overleftrightarrow{YZ}$, or $\overleftrightarrow{XZ}$

7. Equiangular hexagon

8. Supplementary angles

9. Median of a triangle

10. Parallelogram

13. Altitude

16. Regular pentagon

19. Isosceles triangle

22. Base angles

11. Obtuse angle

14. $\overleftrightarrow{PQ}$

17. Rhombus

20. Acute triangle

23. $\angle XYZ$ or $\angle ZYX$

12. Angle bisector

15. $\overrightarrow{MN}$

18. $\overline{PQ}$

21. Linear pair

24. Complementary angles

Chapter 3

Practice 1

1. f

4. g

7. j

10. d

2. b

5. a

8. c

11. i

3. h

6. e

9. l

12. k

Chapter 4

Practice 1

1. Trapezoid

3. Right triangle

5. Quadrilateral

7. Trapezoid

9. Rectangle
   (also a square and a rhombus)

2. Parallelogram

4. Rectangle

6. Right isosceles triangle

8. Parallelogram

10. Parallelogram
    (also a rhombus)

11.

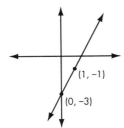

12.

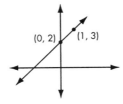

13.

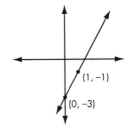

14.

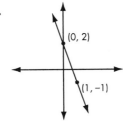

15.

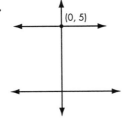

16.

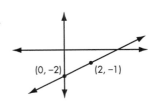

17.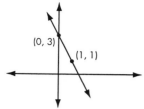

(0, 3)
(1, 1)

18.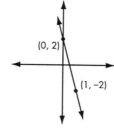

(0, 2)
(1, −2)

19.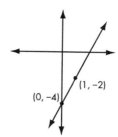

(1, −2)
(0, −4)

20.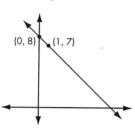

(0, 8) (1, 7)

21. $y = \frac{7}{3}x + \frac{8}{3}$

22. $x = 4$

23. $y = -x - 2$

24. $y = x + 1$

25. $y = -1$

26. $y = -3x - 1$

27. $y = \frac{1}{2}x - \frac{3}{2}$

28. $y = -\frac{1}{3}x + 4$

Practice 2

1. (2, 1)

2. (1, 4)

3. (4, 5)

4. (4, 7)

5. (−3, −5)

6. (1, 2)

7. (4, −1)

8. (8, −1)

9. (1, −1)

10. (2, 3)

11. Centroid: (0, 1)
Circumcenter: (1, 0)
Orthocenter: (−2, 3)

12. Centroid: $(\frac{5}{3}, 1)$
Circumcenter: $(4, \frac{1}{2})$
Orthocenter: (−3, 2)

13. Centroid: $(\frac{2}{3}, \frac{1}{3})$
Circumcenter: $(\frac{1}{2}, 0)$
Orthocenter: (1, 1)

14. Centroid: (0, 5)
Circumcenter: $(-\frac{5}{6}, \frac{25}{6})$
Orthocenter: $(\frac{5}{3}, \frac{20}{3})$

15. Centroid: $(\frac{2}{3}, \frac{28}{3})$
Circumcenter: $(\frac{7}{5}, \frac{43}{5})$
Orthocenter: $(-\frac{4}{5}, \frac{54}{5})$

16. Centroid: $(\frac{5}{3}, -1)$
Circumcenter: $(\frac{11}{14}, -1)$
Orthocenter: $(\frac{24}{7}, -1)$

Chapter 5

Practice 1

1. Yes

2. Yes

3. No

4. No

5. No

6. Yes

7. $a < b < e < d < c$

8. $a < c < b$

9. $a < b < c$

10. $c < a < b$

11. $a < b < c$

12. $w > y$, $m\angle a = 62°$, $m\angle b = 65°$, $m\angle c = 50°$

13. $b > a$, $m\angle c = 57°$, $m\angle d = 76°$

Practice 2

1. SSS

2. SAS

3. SSS

4. $\triangle TEN$ (SAS)

5. $\triangle HPD$ (SSS)

6. $\triangle IBT$ (SAS)

7. $\triangle CBD$ (SSS)

8. Cannot be determined.

9. Cannot be determined.

10. $\triangle DCB$ (SAS)

11. $\triangle IAN$ (SSS)

12. Cannot be determined.

13. ASA

14. AAS

15. SAS

16. $\triangle OWB$ (SAS)

17. $\triangle NRA$ (AAS)

18. $\triangle MEA$ (ASA)

19. Cannot be determined.

20. $\triangle ENB$ (SAS)

21. $\triangle EGQ$ (ASA)

22. $\triangle SUT$ (SAS)

23. $\triangle DFC$ (AAS)

24. $\triangle GQK$ (ASA)

Chapter 6

Practice 1

1. $55°$

2. 5

3. 11

4. 3

5. 16

6. 42

7. $(2, 4)$

8. $(0, -3)$

9. $(4, 0)$

10. $(6, 2)$

11. $(0, -6)$

12. $(8, 4)$

13. $a = 50°$, $b = 80°$, $c = 100°$, $d = 80°$, $e = 170°$, $f = 10°$, $g = 85°$, $h = 47.5°$, $i = 132.5°$, $k = 47.5°$, $m = 170°$, $n = 95°$

Chapter 7

Practice 1

1. $m\angle XNM = 40°$
$m\overarc{XN} = 180°$
$m\overarc{MN} = 100°$

2. $x = 120°$
$y = 60°$
$z = 120°$

3. $a = 90°$
$b = 55°$

4. $a = 50°$
$b = 60°$
$c = 70°$

5. $x = 140°$

6. $m\angle A = 90°$
$m\overarc{AB} = 72°$
$m\angle C = 36°$
$m\overarc{CB} = 108°$

7. $m\overarc{AD} = 140°$
$m\angle D = 30°$
$m\overarc{AB} = 60°$
$m\overarc{DAB} = 200°$

8. $m\angle ABC = 115°$
$m\overarc{AD} = 95°$
$m\overarc{DC} = 150°$
$m\overarc{ADC} = 245°$
$m\overarc{ACD} = 265°$

9. $a = 50°$, $b = 50°$, $c = 80°$, $d = 50°$, $e = 130°$, $f = 90°$, $g = 50°$, $h = 50°$, $j = 90°$, $k = 40°$, $m = 80°$, $n = 50°$, $p = 130°$

10. 21π cm

11. 12.5 cm

12. 9.6 cm

13. 12π cm

14. 60π cm

15. 24 cm

16. $2\sqrt{2}\pi$ cm

Practice 2

1. 4π

4. $\dfrac{35\pi}{9}$

7. $\dfrac{100\pi}{9}$

10. 396

2. 4π

5. $\dfrac{80\pi}{9}$

8. 31.5

3. 30

6. 6.25π

9. 22π

Chapter 9

Practice 1

1. 240 tiles

2. No. The carpet's area is 180 square feet, and the room's area is 206.25 ft². Thus, there is not enough carpet to completely fill the room.

3. 7.1″

4. 3.5 cm

5. 5.0 cm

6. 11.0 cm

7. 1 gal, 2 qt. The room's area, including the ceiling, is 584 ft². To buy full cans of paints, round up to 1 gal, 2 qt.

8. Answers will vary. Possible answers: 50′ or 57′. Minimum number of seams is 2.

9. 12π cm

10. 20.25π cm²

11. 3 cm

12. $\dfrac{6}{\pi}$ cm

Practice 2

1. 25π cm

4. $198\dfrac{2}{3}\pi$ cm

7. 24π ft²

2. 21π cm

5. 1792 in.²

8. 310 m²

3. 40π cm

6. 288 cm²

Chapter 10

Practice 1

1. 26 cm

4. 48 cm

7. 36″

2. 15 cm

5. Yes

8. $a = 10\sqrt{2}$ cm, $b = 5\sqrt{6}$ cm

3. 3 cm

6. No

9. $c = 10\sqrt{3}$ cm, $d = 5\sqrt{3}$ cm

10. $e = 5\sqrt{6}$ cm, $f = 5\sqrt{6}$ cm   **11.** $\left(\dfrac{-1}{2}, \dfrac{\sqrt{3}}{2}\right)$ **12.** $\left(-\dfrac{\sqrt{2}}{2}, -\dfrac{\sqrt{2}}{2}\right)$

Practice 2

1. 8 cm
2. $(-6\sqrt{3}, 6)$
3. $(8\sqrt{2}, 8\sqrt{2})$
4. Isosceles, 32 units
5. $M(7, 10)$, $N(10, 14)$, $P(13, 10)$
6. The slopes are the same.
7. $PN = 5$, $AB = 10$; AB is twice PN.
8. $x^2 + (y + 3)^2 = 25$

Chapter 11

Practice 1

1. 150π cm^3
2. 12 cm^2
3. 516 cm^3
4. 192 cm^3
5. 768π cm^3
6. $75x^3$ cm^3
7. $432\sqrt{2}$ cm^3
8. 15 cm

Practice 2

1. 2.304π m^3
2. 12π m^2
3. $V = 10{,}752$ cm^3, $S = 3{,}008$ cm^2
4. $V = 48$ cm^3, $S = 96$ cm^2
5. $V = 1771$ cm^3, $S = 938$ cm^2
6. $V = 144\pi$ cm^3, $S = 72\pi$ cm^2
7. 1.5 cm
8. 6 cm

Chapter 12

Practice 1

1. 1:4
2. 1:4
3. A little more than 42 gal
4. $2.5'' \times 4.375''$
5. $AP = 8$ cm, $EI = 7$ cm, $SR = 15$ cm, $YW = 12$ cm
6. 10.5 cm

7. $TS = 15$ cm, $QP = 51$ cm
8. Yes
9. 27'

Practice 2

1. AA Similarity Conjecture
2. 64 cm
3. 16:25
4. 2:3
5. 8:125
6. 3:4
7. $\frac{1}{4}$
8. 22.5 cm
9. 20 cm
10. 8.75 cm
11. $6\frac{2}{7}$ cm

Chapter 13

Practice 1

1. 10 cm
2. 24 cm
3. 35°
4. 22°
5. 62'
6. 15"
7. 28°
8. 90'
9. 17 cm
10. 53°
11. 17"
12. 8'
13. 23°
14. 28°
15. 4 m
16. 31°
17. 493 ft
18. 35 in.
19. 34°
20. 7"

Chapter 14

Practice 1

1. MT
2. MP
3. LC
4. MT
5. MP
6. LS
7. MT
8. LC and MT
9. MT
10. MP and MT
11. No valid conclusion
12. MT and MP twice

Introduction to the Additional Geometry Projects

The twenty-one projects in this section were collected from *Discovering Geometry* classrooms across the country. Many of these projects are among the *Discovering Geometry* field testers' favorites, and they include geometry review games, art projects, a topology project, and a map-coloring project. Some projects were written specifically for a particular chapter. Others are general-interest projects you can use with any chapter of the book. Below is a short description of each project. For information on assessing projects, refer to the section Assessment in the *Teacher's Guide and Answer Key*.

Perspective Drawing projects

These three projects—**Block Lettering in Perspective**, **Perspective View of a Tiled Floor**, and **Spacing Fenceposts in Perspective**—are extensions to Project: Drawing a High-Rise Complex in Chapter 0. Students learn to draw block lettering, a tiled floor in perspective, and a sequence of fence posts in perspective.

Beehive Geometry

Students look for patterns in sequences of connected hexagons. This project extends the patterns students find as they observe sequences of squares and rectangles in Chapter 1.

Geopardy

This is a game adapted from the television show *Jeopardy,* and is an alternative way to review for a chapter test or a semester final. The project features a complete set of questions for a Chapter 2 review, but you can adapt the game for use with any chapter.

Stained Glass

This project provides student and teacher instructions for creating an original geometric design and painting it on glass. Students enjoy this project because they make connections between geometry and art and create something decorative that other students and teachers will see and admire. You can use this project with Chapter 0, 3, or 8.

Map Coloring

This project explores the classic map-coloring problem and a few simple extensions. It is a general-interest project that you can use with any chapter in the book.

Occupational Speaker

This project contains student guidelines for inviting a guest speaker to give a class presentation about how she or he use geometry in her or his job. It is a general-interest project that is appropriate at any point in the curriculum.

Matho

Matho is a game adapted from the game of bingo. Students fill in the Matho game board with teacher-supplied answers to review questions, then cross off the answers as they solve the questions during the course of the game. The project features a complete set of answers and questions for a Chapter 6 review, but you can adapt the game for use with any chapter.

Folding Paper Circles

In this project students explore some simple geometric ideas by folding paper circles. You can use the project in several ways: as a mid-unit or end-of-chapter review activity for Chapter 7, as an informal end-of-chapter assessment project for Chapter 7, or as an early introduction to justification and proof. Once students complete the project, they can use their folded circles as reference tools when they study similar figures.

Symmetry in Snowflakes

Many students remember creating paper snowflakes in elementary school to decorate their classroom windows and to give as gifts. This project allows them to enjoy that activity again *and* to incorporate the geometric concepts and vocabulary they've learned in their mathematics class. The project works best in Chapter 8 because it explores ideas of symmetry and the relationship between angle measures and polygon shapes, but you can also use it with earlier chapters.

Tessellation T-shirts

This project features a complete set of teacher and student instructions for transferring a tessellation design to a T-shirt. You can use the project with any chapter, but it works best with the two chapters on geometric art, Chapters 0 and 8.

Building a Home

Students use the floor plan of a home to estimate the cost of various finishing jobs such as painting, carpeting, and tiling. To estimate the costs, students must contact suppliers, provide samples, and justify their choices. The project is a natural extension of some of the problems in Chapter 9.

Finding Another Proof of the Pythagorean Theorem

Students research a Pythagorean Theorem proof that they have not studied in class, then present and explain the proof. You can use this project with Chapter 10 or when students explore geometric proof in Chapters 14–16.

Packing Efficiency and Displacement

Students use displacement to measure the volume of a light bulb and of a tube of toothpaste, then measure the volume of the light bulb and toothpaste packing materials to calculate their packing efficiency. Finally, students create a poster to show their results. This project is an extension of the material in Chapter 11.

Grow Creatures projects

Grow Creatures are toys that expand when placed in water. In the project **Similarity in Grow Creatures** students use their knowledge of similar figures to determine if a pair of three-dimensional figures are similar. The project **Grow Creatures Growth Patterns** allows for the collection and analysis of data over time and for the use of graphing calculators. These projects are extensions of the material in Chapter 12.

The Geometry of Baseball

In this project students use geometry to lay out a baseball diamond. This project works well with Chapter 6 or 13. If you use it with Chapter 13, students can use trigonometry to complete the project.

A Möbius Strip: The Surface with a Twist

Students make a Möbius strip and answer some questions about it. This project is a general-interest project, but it is probably best to use in the later chapters of the book once students have developed their geometric vocabulary.

Writing a Logic Puzzle

Students learn to write logic puzzles similar to those in Chapter 14. This project is fairly difficult and may be better for more advanced students.

Proof by Mathematical Induction

This is a very challenging topic. You may want to reserve this project for your more mathematically ambitious students. Make sure students appreciate that mathematical induction is a method of proof and therefore a form of deductive reasoning—it's easy to get the *induction* in the term *mathematical induction* confused with the *inductive* in the term *inductive reasoning*. Use this project with Chapters 15 and 16.

Project Contributors

Masha Albrecht is an editor and workshop leader for Key Curriculum Press. She has taught high school in various parts of the country and was a writer for the Systemic Initiative for Montana Math and Science (SIMMS) project. Masha leads workshops on using the Lénárt Sphere materials and The Geometer's Sketchpad software with students.

Ralph Bothe is mathematics department chair at Edward C. Reed High School in Sparks, Nevada. He has been teaching geometry for twenty-seven years and has been involved with *Discovering Geometry* for the past six years. Ralph attended one of the first Key Curriculum Press institutes in Berkeley, California, has done consulting work for Key Curriculum, and field tested the second edition of *Discovering Geometry*.

Sharon Grand taught for twenty-five years in East Baton Rouge Parish, Louisiana, before joining Key Curriculum Press in 1996 as an educational consultant. She was a 1990 winner of the Presidential Award for Excellence in Science and Mathematics Teaching, the 1991 Louisiana High School Teacher of the Year, and a 1993 Tandy Technology Teacher. Sharon leads inservices and workshops, and is a lead instructor for the Discovering Geometry Summer Institutes.

Judy Hicks is a mathematics and computer science teacher at Standley Lake High School in Westminster, Colorado. She has been teaching for twenty-four years, and since 1989 she has taught local, state, and national Sketchpad inservices. She currently does consulting work for Key Curriculum Press.

Darlene Pugh has been teaching math and science at Malta High School in northern Montana for twenty-two years. She was a writer for the Systemic Initiative for Montana Math and Science (SIMMS) project.

Eberhard Scheiffele received his Ph.D. from the University of California, Berkeley, in the logic and methodology of science. He taught mathematics at the University of San Francisco; the University of California, Berkeley; the University of Michigan, Ann Arbor; the University of Texas, Austin; and the University of Freiburg in Germany. Eberhard also taught geometry for the Upward Bound program at Holy Names College in Oakland, California.

Carolyn Sessions is a teacher at University High School in Baton Rouge, Louisiana. She has been using *Discovering Geometry* since 1990 and is a presenter at Discovering Geometry institutes and workshops. Carolyn is a Presidential Awardee for Excellence in Science and Mathematics Teaching and a Tandy Technology Outstanding Teacher.

Luis Shein, Key Curriculum Press's production manager, is also a mathematician who studied in Mexico and Berkeley, California. He did his doctorate work in differential topology under the guidance of Professor Shiing-shen Chern. Luis appreciates the beauty of mathematical ideas and has worked as a teacher, developing multimedia presentations and lectures on mathematical ideas. He is particularly interested in the didactic history and philosophy of mathematics.

Block Lettering in Perspective

Michael Serra

Perspective drawing techniques can be used to create letters or words that appear to be three-dimensional. This is useful for giving emphasis to an element of a design. Your task in this special project is to draw letters or words with one-point and two-point perspectives.

Drawing Block Letters in One-Point Perspective

Step 1

Write a word in block letters. Draw a horizon line parallel to the bottom edge of your word. Select a vanishing point on the horizon line.

Step 2

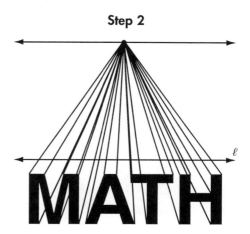

Draw vanishing lines from all corner points of the block letters back to the vanishing point. Select a thickness for your block letters and draw a line (line ℓ) parallel to the horizon line.

Step 3

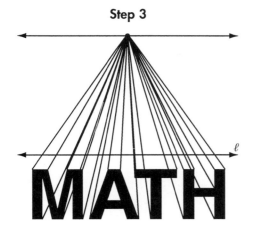

To create the back edges of your letters, draw lines parallel to the front edges, starting and ending on the points where line ℓ intersects the vanishing lines.

Step 4

Erase all the vanishing lines and shade in all the sides and tops of the letters.

Now try making block letters. Draw a perspective view of your name or initials in block letters. You can change the perspective by making the horizon line high or low and by placing the vanishing point at the left or right.

Drawing Block Letters in Two-Point Perspective

Step 1

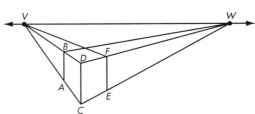

Draw a box in two-point perspective. Label the points as shown. Make the height *CD* and the width *CE* of your box about the same. (For example, *CD* = *CE* = 6 cm.) Do not erase the vanishing lines. Your first letter will fill the front face of this box. Select a distance between the first and second letters by drawing a vertical line *GH*. If you used 6 cm for the width *CE*, use about 1 cm for *EG*.

Step 2

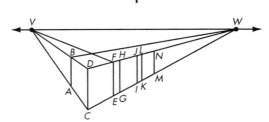

Select a width for your second box by drawing a vertical segment *IJ*. This box will eventually house your second letter. If you used 6 cm for *CE*, use about 3 cm for *GI*. Next, select a width for the space between the second and third boxes by drawing in a vertical segment *KL*. If you used 1 cm for *EG*, use 0.5 cm for *IK*. Repeat this procedure for the third box.

Step 3

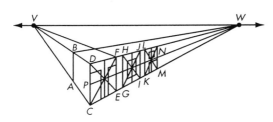

Now design a letter on the front face of each box. Draw in diagonal lines *CF, DE, HI, GJ, LM,* and *KN*. The points where these diagonals intersect are the perspective centers for each front face. Draw vertical lines through these centers. Label the center in the first box *P*. Draw line *PW*. Use this line to center each block letter on its front face.

Step 4

Draw all the top vanishing lines from the top front corners to the back edges of the solid letters. Draw all the vertical edges at the backs of the solid letters. Draw all the remaining vanishing lines. With a pen or felt-tip marker, outline all the edges of the solid letters. Erase all other lines. Decorate.

Draw a two-point perspective view of your name or initials in solid letters.

Perspective View of a Tiled Floor

Michael Serra

Step 1

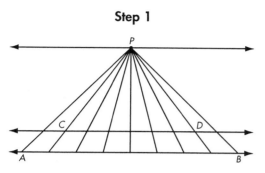

Draw a pair of horizontal parallel lines. The upper line is your horizon line. The lower line will become the front edge of your first row of squares. On the lower line, mark off eight equal lengths. Label the endpoints A and B. On the top line (your horizon line), select a vanishing point P. Draw all nine vanishing lines. Draw a line parallel to line AB and the horizon line. This line determines the back edge of your first row of squares. Label points C and D as shown in the diagram.

Step 2

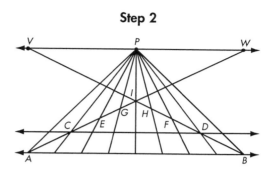

Draw diagonal segments BD and AC and extend them to the horizon line. Label the points where these diagonals intersect the horizon line as V and W. Diagonal segments BV and AW should both cross through the center vanishing line at the same point I. Mark off points where diagonal segments BV and AW intersect the nine vanishing lines. Label the intersections as shown.

Step 3

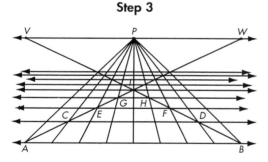

Draw a line through points E and F. This is the back line for the second row of squares. Draw a line through points G and H. This is the back line for the third row of squares. Draw a line through point I parallel to the other horizontal lines. This is the back edge of the fourth row. Continue in this fashion, drawing lines through pairs of points until all nine horizontal lines have been drawn.

Step 4

Shade in alternating squares. Erase all unnecessary portions of horizontal and vanishing lines. For a special effect, you may add a slim rectangle to the front of the tile pattern to give it thickness.

Spacing Fenceposts in Perspective

Michael Serra

Step 1

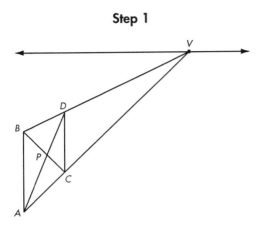

Start with a horizon line and vanishing point V. Draw the fencepost nearest the viewer and label it segment AB. Draw vanishing lines from the top and bottom of the post. Draw the second post parallel to the first at a distance from it that looks pleasing to you. Label it segment CD. Draw the diagonal segments AD and BC. The diagonals intersect at a point. Label it P.

Step 2

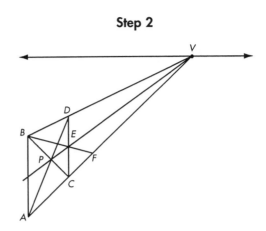

Draw a line connecting point P and the vanishing point. This line will pass through the centers of all the posts. Draw a line from point B through point E, the center of the second post. Extend it until it meets the bottom vanishing line AV. Call this point F. Point F is the base of the third post.

Step 3

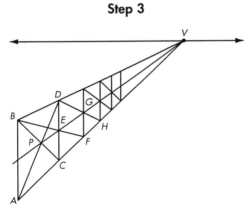

Continue in this way, drawing a line through points D and G. Point G is the middle point of the third post. Extend this line until it intersects the vanishing line AV at a point called H. This new point is the base of the fourth post. Continue until you have all the posts you want.

Step 4

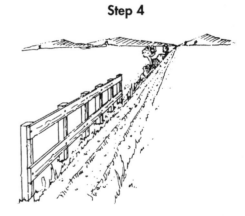

Use these lines as a guide to draw in the complete fence.

Beehive Geometry

Michael Serra

In earlier lessons, you looked for patterns in sequences of squares and rectangles. In this project, you will look for patterns in sequences of hexagons. In the exercises for this project, pretend that the darker-colored hexagons are potential homes for queen bees in a honeycomb. Try the following exercises.

1. If the pattern of hexagons continues in the hexagon grid, how many non–queen bee cells will there be (no pun intended) when there are 80 queen bee cells?

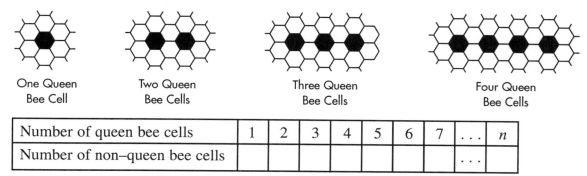

Number of queen bee cells	1	2	3	4	5	6	7	. . .	n
Number of non–queen bee cells								. . .	

2. This pattern shows the growth pattern for a beehive for the first four weeks. If the pattern continues, how many queen bee cells will there be after the tenth week? How many non–queen bee cells will there be after the tenth week?

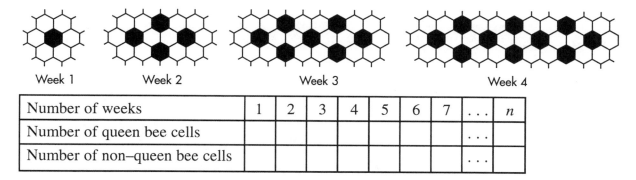

Number of weeks	1	2	3	4	5	6	7	. . .	n
Number of queen bee cells								. . .	
Number of non–queen bee cells								. . .	

3. This pattern shows the growth pattern for a beehive for the first four weeks. The worker bees working on this honeycomb are not as linear in their thinking as those in Exercises 1 and 2. They are building their pattern of queen bee cells in three directions. If the pattern continues, how many queen bee cells will there be after the tenth week? How many non–queen bee cells after the tenth week?

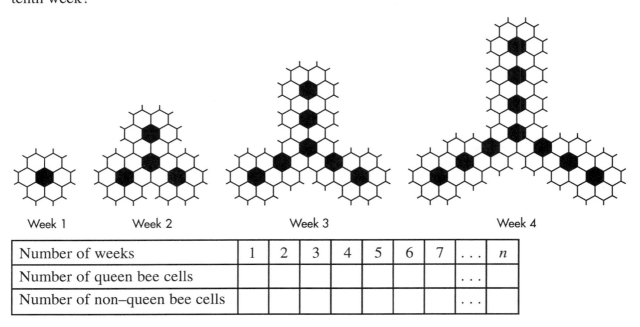

Week 1   Week 2   Week 3   Week 4

Number of weeks	1	2	3	4	5	6	7	. . .	n
Number of queen bee cells								. . .	
Number of non–queen bee cells								. . .	

4. This pattern shows the growth pattern for a beehive for the first four weeks. The worker bees working on this honeycomb are building near a freeway and are used to seeing signs that tell humans what they cannot do ("Do Not Enter," "Do Not Trespass"). The worker bees therefore have decided to build their honeycomb pattern to tell humans, "Do not stop here!" If the pattern continues, how many queen bee cells will there be on the boundary, or perimeter, after the tenth week? How many queen bee cells will there be on the diagonal after the tenth week? How many queen bee cells will there be altogether after the tenth week?

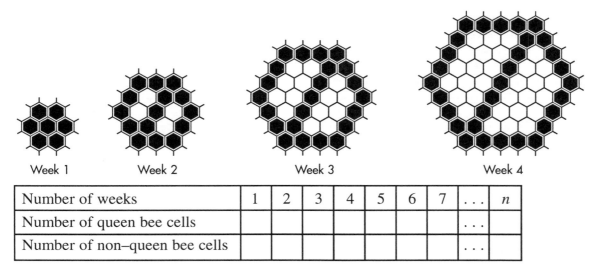

Week 1   Week 2   Week 3   Week 4

Number of weeks	1	2	3	4	5	6	7	. . .	n
Number of queen bee cells								. . .	
Number of non–queen bee cells								. . .	

5. On hexagonal grid paper, design the first four terms of your own beehive pattern. Find a rule for your pattern.

Beehive Geometry

Hexagonal Grid

Geopardy

Judy Hicks

Teacher notes

This game is adapted from the popular television game show. It is an alternative way to review for a chapter test or a semester final. The material in this particular project is a complete set of materials for a Chapter 2 Geopardy game. You can use this as a model to write a Geopardy game as a chapter review for any other chapter in the text.

Another variation is to have groups of students make up cards for particular subjects or particular chapters. You may want to add a few trivia questions that pertain only to your class. When your students make up their questions, they should also write the answer to each question. This way you will have many different cards to choose from. However, take care that their questions are not difficult or confusing.

Depending on your computer experience, this entire activity can also be done on the computer. HyperCard™, Hyperstudio™, Linkway™, or similar software can be used to simulate the game. All scoring and so on can be done electronically. Music and other sound effects can easily be included for fun. The computer can then be connected to a monitor for all the students to see. Another variation is to have several computers set up and have students play against each other at each computer.

Materials

- One blank Geopardy scoresheet for each student.

- A transparency with the categories and points. Bring in a marker that you can use to cross off the questions.

- One set of review questions and answers.

Suggested Rules

1. Divide the class into three teams.

2. Give each person a blank Geopardy sheet (big enough for work to be shown).

3. Assign each person a random number between 1 and the number of students in the class. This can easily be done with a calculator ahead of time.

4. Roll a die (or use the calculator) to determine which team starts. Again, use the calculator to randomly choose the person on that team to pick a category and value.

5. Uncover a question on the overhead (or read it).

6. All the students must work each problem.

7. The person chosen may confer with his or her team before answering. If the answer is correct, that team receives points. If the answer is incorrect, another team has the chance to answer. The teacher may choose to go over some questions now or later.

8. If the team answers the question correctly and receives points, the team score is adjusted accordingly. Post each team's overall score on the board.

9. For the next question, again randomly pick a new team and person, or just go around in order and follow the same directions.

---

10. The Geopardy board should include two "daily doubles." For a "daily double," the team and person chosen may bet a maximum of 50 points if their score is less than the amount of the selection picked. If they have more, they can only bet up to double the amount of the selection. If their answer is correct, the overall score is increased by double the bet. If it is incorrect, their score is decreased by the amount of the bet.

11. When there is about 10 minutes left, every team and member plays "Final Geopardy." Each team is notified of the category and asked to write the amount of its bet on its geopardy card. Each team must cooperatively make this decision. It may only bet up to the amount of points it has in its account (or 50 points, if it has less than 50). The question is then displayed. After a certain amount of time, each team must decide on the answer and its members must write the answer on their papers. All sheets are then passed in. The teacher will choose one paper (from each team) from which to read the answer and add or subtract the points from the team's score accordingly.

12. The winning team's members receive a "bonus buck," which can be used to excuse tardiness, or as bonus points or assignment points, or for candy, and so on.

Example Questions for Chapter 2

Angles for:

10—An angle whose measure is 90 degrees.

  What is a right angle?

20—An angle whose measure is less than 90 degrees.

  What is an acute angle?

30—An angle whose measure is greater than 90 degrees.

  What is an obtuse angle?

40—An example that proves a statement wrong.

  What is a counterexample?

50—A statement in which a conditional statement and its converse are both true and are combined into one statement.

  What is a biconditional statement?

Angles and Lines for:

10—Two or more lines that lie in the same plane and do not intersect.

  What are parallel lines?

20—Two lines that intersect to form a right triangle.

  What are perpendicular lines?

30—Two angles whose measures have the sum of 90 degrees.

  What are complementary angles?

40—Two angles whose measures have the sum of 180 degrees.

  What are supplementary angles?

50—A ray that divides an angle into two congruent angles.

  What is an angle bisector?

Example Questions for Chapter 2

Polygons and Such for:

10—A five-sided polygon.

What is a pentagon?

20—A polygon whose sides are equal in measure.

What is an equilateral polygon?

30—A polygon in which no segment connecting two vertices is outside the polygon.

What is a convex polygon?

40—A ten-sided polygon.

What is a decagon?

50—Two sides of a polygon that share a common vertex.

What are consecutive sides?

Triangles for:

10—A triangle with exactly one right angle.

What is a right triangle?

20—A triangle with three acute angles.

What is an acute triangle?

30—A triangle with exactly one obtuse angle.

What is an obtuse triangle?

40—A triangle with at least two sides the same length.

What is an isosceles triangle?

50—A segment connecting the midpoint of a side to the opposite vertex.

What is a median?

Example Questions for Chapter 2

Quadrilaterals for:

10—A quadrilateral in which both pairs of opposite sides are parallel.

   What is a parallelogram?

20—An equilateral parallelogram.

   What is a rhombus?

30—A quadrilateral with exactly two pairs of distinct congruent consecutive sides.

   What is a kite?

40—A quadrilateral with exactly one pair of parallel sides.

   What is a trapezoid?

50—An equiangular rhombus or an equilateral rectangle.

   What is a square?

Potpourri for:

10—Two or more points that lie on the same line.

   What are collinear points?

20—A unit of measure for angles.

   What is a degree?

30—Lines that are not in the same plane and that do not intersect.

   What are skew lines?

40—A closed geometric figure in a plane in which line segments connect endpoint to endpoint and each segment intersects exactly two others.

   What is a polygon?

Example Questions for Chapter 2

50—An 11-sided polygon.

What is an undecagon?

Final Geopardy:

Category: Potpourri

A perpendicular segment from a vertex to the opposite side or the line containing the opposite side.

What is an altitude?

Geopardy

ANGLES	ANGLES & LINES	POLYGONS & SUCH	TRIANGLES	QUADS	POTPOURRI	TRIVIA

Name _____   Final Geopardy Answer _____

Team _____   Bet _____

Geopardy

ANGLES	ANGLES & LINES	POLYGONS & SUCH	TRIANGLES	QUADS	POTPOURRI	TRIVIA
10	10	10	10	10	10	10
20	20	20	20	20	20	20
30	30	30	30	30	30	30
40	40	40	40	40	40	40
50	50	50	50	50	50	50

Stained Glass

Sharon Grand and Carolyn Sessions

Teacher notes

Beginning in Chapter 3: Using the Tools of Geometry, students acquire and practice construction skills requiring the use of compass and straightedge or patty paper. Constructions are used to lead to students' discovering geometric relationships and making conjectures; this project reinforces these skills and allows students to combine them with their creativity and artistic talents.

"Stained glass" is really painting on glass: a water-based simulated liquid leading is used to outline the constructed design, and then the outlined areas are colored by filling them with water-based glass paints, or "stains." The paints become clear or translucent when dry, so when the finished pieces are hung in a window, they have the appearance of stained glass.

This project is popular with students because they not only review geometry concepts and use problem-solving skills to plan and create their designs, but they also connect geometry and art to create something decorative that others will see and admire. Students who might not be great successes academically can shine with this project. Many have reported that they still have their stained glass pieces even years after graduating from high school.

The stained glass instructions can be used for a variety of student work that has been designed on paper: compass-and-straightedge designs, tessellations, geometric art designs. It is difficult to work with designs that have very small areas to put color into. Designs can be originals or re-creations of designs in construction books or posters. This project could also be adapted for use with Chapter 0: Geometric Art and Chapter 8: Transformations and Tessellations.

It is helpful to work in a room with access to water to make cleanup easier. A science lab with faucets and table is ideal. The finished pieces can be collected in an eye-catching display. Rather than putting the glass into the frame, affix two 1-in. strips of double-sided foam tape to the back of the glass. Press them onto the window glass. These can be removed by inserting a thin flexible blade (such as a palette knife) between the two pieces of glass to break the foam tape.

Materials

Each student group will need one set of the following:

- Water-based glass stains
- Small water-color brushes
- One small bottle of liquid leading (water-based) per group of four students
- Dish soap to clean brushes
- Newspaper to protect surfaces from paint
- Eyedroppers
- Cotton swabs
- Compass or large safety pin
- Scissors
- An 8-×-10-in. piece of clear glass or an 8-×-10-in. wall picture frame with regular glass. The picture frame should be a wooden frame that has staples on the back to keep the glass in. Do not get a frame with non-glare glass!

Stained Glass

Sharon Grand and Carolyn Sessions

In this project, you will transfer a geometric design onto glass and create a stained-glass window. It is difficult to work with designs that have very small areas to put color into. Keep this in mind when you create your design. Designs can be originals or recreations of designs in construction books or posters. Look in Chapter 0: Geometric Art and Chapter 8: Transformations and Tessellations for some ideas.

At-Home Preparation

1. You will need an 8-×-10-in. piece of regular glass. Do not get nonglare glass, or the stain will not stick to the glass. You can purchase an 8-×-10-in. wooden picture frame that has staples on the back to keep the glass in place. This way, you will have a frame ready for your stained glass when you have finished the project.

2. Place masking tape around all the edges of the glass so that you won't cut yourself or someone else with an edge.

3. Wash the glass with soap and water. Do not use glass cleaner, or the paint will not stick to the glass. Dry the glass thoroughly with a paper towel or lint-free towel. If you bought glass in a frame, take the glass out of the frame before washing it.

4. Wrap the glass in several layers of newspaper and tape it securely around the glass.

5. Put the glass (and the frame, if you bought one) into a paper bag and bring it to school. Bring some extra newspaper to cover your desk.

6. Dress in old clothes on painting day. The paint may stain your clothes.

7. You should draw or construct a geometric design to use on the glass. Look in Chapter 0: Geometric Art and Chapter 8: Transformations and Tessellations for some ideas. The design should fit into a rectangle that is about an inch smaller than the glass in both directions. Otherwise, the frame may cover part of your design. Use watercolors or Magic Markers to select colors for your design.

How to Paint the Design onto the Glass

Make sure that your group has the following items:

- One geometric design per student

- Water-based glass stains

- Small water-color brushes

- One small bottle of liquid leading (water based)

- Newspaper to protect surfaces from paint

- Eyedroppers

- Cotton swabs

- Compass or large safety pin
- Scissors
- Glass

Instructions for Painting the Glass

1. Clear your workspace of unnecessary items and place a protective layer of newspaper on it. Place your design on the table and put the glass on top of it. Arrange the glass until the design is aligned the way that you would like it to appear on the glass when painted.

2. Tape the design to the glass at the upper and lower edges so that the paper will not move while you are painting.

3. Get a bottle of liquid leading. Cut the end of the nozzle. After recapping it, shake the bottle so that the liquid leading fills the nozzle. On a sheet of newspaper, practice making a smooth line of "lead" come out of the nozzle. Squeeze with even pressure and try to hold your hand steady. Try resting the tip of the nozzle on the paper and holding the bottle at an angle and slowly dragging it across the paper. When you are confident with the leading, you can use the same technique to apply your design to the glass.

4. Use the liquid leading to outline your design on the glass. Do not worry if all of the lines are not uniform in size. Make the lines rather thick. If there are any breaks in the lines, go back and fill them in. Use a pencil point or a compass to reopen the nozzle if it clogs up.

5. If possible, let the liquid leading dry overnight. Otherwise, begin adding the paint stain to your design.

6. Use an eyedropper or water-color brush to paint the areas between the lines of leading. You want to make as thick a coat of paint as possible without having it spill over the lines into adjacent regions. Eyedroppers are helpful in removing air bubbles; cotton swabs are useful in cleaning up spills. Make sure that the stain adheres to the edges of the leading strips.

7. Let the paint dry overnight. When your stained glass is completely dry, you can hang it in a window, either by using double-sided foam tape or by attaching a chain and small screws.

Map Coloring

Masha Albrecht and Darlene Pugh

This project consists of five parts and is really a collection of five short projects that build in difficulty. You can choose from this collection. The projects probably make the most sense if you do them in the order in which they appear.

Materials

- 1-m piece of string (Part 2)
- Crayons or pencils of at least 6 different colors (Parts 1, 2, and 3)
- Blank sheets of unlined paper (Parts 2 and 3)
- Copies of the map of the U.S. (Part 1)
- Cellophane tape (Part 2)
- A torus (Part 5)
- Research materials, from a library or the World Wide Web (Part 4)

Part 1

Coloring the Map of the U.S.

A cartographer is someone who makes maps. Suppose you are a cartographer and your job is to color a map of all the states in the United States. To make each state easy to distinguish from the others, states that share a border cannot be the same color, but states that just touch at a corner point can be the same color. Follow these rules to color the map of the United States provided by your teacher. As you color the map, determine your best answers to these two questions:

1. What is the least number of colors you need to color the map of the United States?
2. What is the least number of colors you need to color any map on the earth?

Part 2

Coloring Two Special Kinds of Maps

The least number of colors needed to color a map is called the **chromatic number** of the map. (The prefix *chroma-* is from the Greek word for *color*.) In this section, you will invent two types of maps and find their chromatic numbers.

1. On an unlined sheet of paper, randomly draw 10 to 15 straight intersecting lines that go entirely across the paper. Assume the different regions are countries on a map. Color the map with the least number of colors possible. Record the chromatic number of the map.

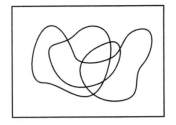

2. Tie a 1-m length of string into a single loop. Drop it onto a piece of plain paper. Use just enough cellophane tape to hold the string in place. Again, think of the different regions as countries on a map. Your map consists only of the regions enclosed by string. Color the map with the least number of colors possible. Record the chromatic number of the map.

3. Compare your answers from the last two problems with those of others who have made the same kinds of maps. If you are working by yourself, make a few more maps using the same two techniques. Record any patterns you observe between the different kinds of maps, and try to explain them.

Part 3

Finding the Largest Chromatic Number of Any Map

In this section, you will explore in more detail the largest number of colors you would ever need if you were a cartographer coloring maps of the earth.

1. Design a simple map of three regions that cannot be colored with only two colors.

2. Design a simple map of four regions that cannot be colored with only three colors.

3. Try to design a map that requires more than four colors. Describe your results.

Part 4

Research Project: The History of the Four-Color Conjecture

Cartographers have known for centuries that they never needed more than four colors to color any map (although they often used more than four colors for convenience). Mathematicians, however, have had a difficult time proving this is true. Research the history of the famous Four-Color Conjecture and write a summary of your findings. Be sure to include a discussion of the controversial computer proof written in 1976 by the mathematicians K. Appel and W. Haken.

Part 5

Extension Project: Maps on the Torus

The surface of a solid that looks like a donut or bagel is called a **torus**. Investigate the largest possible chromatic number of a map on a torus. Hint: It is more than 4!

(Note: If your classroom has a Lénárt Sphere kit, the kit contains a torus. You can draw maps on this torus using dry-erase pens.)

Occupational Speaker

Ralph Bothe

Architects, carpenters, plumbers, doctors, dentists, and artists are all people who use geometry daily. In fact, if you talk to people in different professions, you will be surprised to find out that almost any occupation requires some use of geometry. For this project, you will arrange to have a guest speaker come to your geometry class and do a presentation to the class on how he or she uses geometry in his or her job. This person can be a relative, a friend, or someone else from the community whose profession uses geometry. If you need help finding someone, try contacting volunteer and youth organizations. They may be able to help you identify people who will be interested in coming to a classroom. Once you have identified a person who wants to come to your classroom, set up a time with him or her for you to prepare this person to come to your school.

Interview

Contact the person and schedule a time when it is convenient for the person to spend about 30–45 minutes talking to you. The purpose of this interview is to prepare the speaker to give an overview to the class of all the ways he or she uses geometry. Before you start your interview, you should prepare a list of questions and be prepared to take notes. The leading question in the interview should be "How do you use geometry in your job?" If you are confused by the explanation, be sure to ask questions until you are satisfied that you understand. Remember, this person may not be used to working with students, so be patient and respectful. If this person uses any particular charts or instruments, make sure you understand how they work. Ask the person for help in creating three or more practical problems relating to part of his or her job. Write up the problems on a worksheet and make sure the speaker is prepared to cover them in class.

Preparation

Talk to your geometry teacher and to the guest speaker and find a time that is convenient for the person to visit your class. Before the visit, arrange to have a guest pass for your speaker and a pass from your teacher so that you will be able to meet your guest at the main office when he or she arrives. Make sure the problems you created are included during or after the presentation. All handouts and worksheets should be given to the teacher at least one day before the presentation so that an adequate number of copies can be made. Students will be responsible for all handouts and notes. Any extra equipment that might be necessary should be arranged for at least one day in advance.

Presentation

Meet the speaker at the door or in the main office on the day of your presentation. Introduce the speaker to the teacher and to the class. Assist the speaker with any handouts or equipment. Walk the speaker back to the door when the presentation is over. After the presentation, write a thank-you note to the speaker. Call the speaker a day or so after the presentation, thanking him or her again and asking a few evaluation questions, for instance did you feel the presentation was successful. Prepare and distribute an evaluation survey for your class. Collate your survey results and share them with your teacher and your class. You might want to share them with the speaker as well.

Written Summary

Turn in a written summary of the project to your teacher. This should include a short description of the interview, the name and phone number of the speaker, the problems proposed, your own evaluation, a summary of the class evaluations, copies of all handouts, worksheets, and notes used, and anything else you find significant to the project.

Matho

Masha Albrecht

Teacher Notes

Matho is a game that is based on Bingo. Rather than numbers and letters, students fill their boards with answers to review questions. It works well as a review lesson, but you can play it any time.

It's fun to have small silly prizes ready for the winners. If you prefer, you can also give extra credit to winners. The winners are the first three students to complete a row, a column, or a diagonal on their Matho boards. Also count the last student to complete Matho before the end of class as a winner; otherwise, students may lose interest in the game after the first three winners.

The materials for this project include everything you will need for a Chapter 6 Matho review game. You can make a similar game for any unit by creating different Matho questions and answers.

Materials

- One photocopied matho worksheet per student
- Transparencies of all 24 Matho questions
- Transparency of all 24 Matho answers
- Silly prizes

How to Play

1. Each student should get a blank Matho worksheet when they come to class. Use the overhead to display the answers. Students complete their own Matho boards by randomly copying the 24 answers from the overhead into the 24 spaces on their boards. Students arriving late may forfeit their chance to complete their boards, and thus are less likely to win.

2. Tell students to find and cross off the correct answer as they solve each problem. Have them cross off the free space right away. In order to get Matho, they must have an entire row, column, or diagonal crossed off. As soon as they have done this, they yell "Matho!" At this point, you will check to see if they have crossed off correct answers. If you don't remember which answers are already used up, don't worry; the other students will help you out.

3. Show the first review problem on the overhead. Cover up the other problems with a piece of paper so the class can focus on one problem at a time. Since this is a review day, it's probably worthwhile agreeing on the answer before you move on to the next problem. Some students might just wait until the answer is announced to cross it off their boards. If this becomes a problem, just stop announcing the answers for a few problems.

4. Continue uncovering review problems. Don't hesitate to stop and answer any review questions that students may have along the way. Emphasize that this game is not a race. Most of these Chapter 6 review questions have short answers, so you should be able to get through most of them in a class period. In games such as these, students will have almost the whole board finished (obviously there will be lots of Mathos at that point). It might be unnecessary to give a prize to the last winner, since that would be practically everyone in the class.

5. Hand out the silly prizes to the winners before the end of class.

Matho

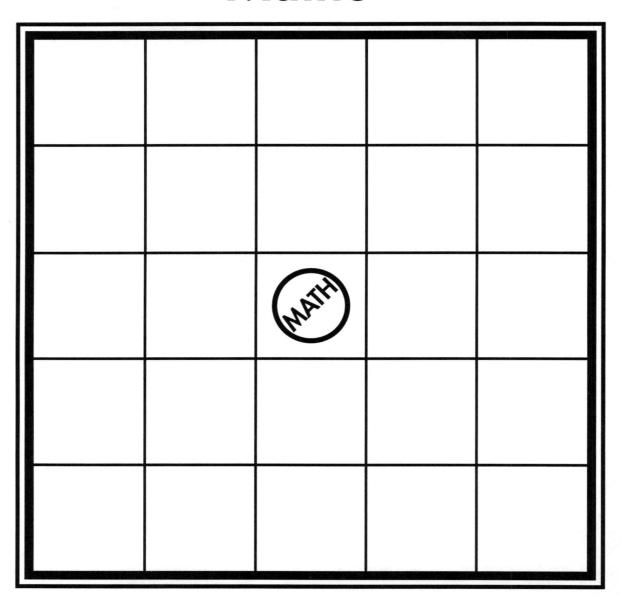

Review Questions

Chapter 6: Polygon Properties

For problems 1–13, complete each statement using the best answer from your Matho board.

1. A quadrilateral with four congruent sides is called a _____.

2. The sum of the measures of the angles of a pentagon is _____.

3. The sum of the measures of the exterior angles of a pentagon is _____.

4. Any angle in a regular octagon measures _____.

5. The measures of the interior angles of a(n) _____ have a sum of 720°.

6. The nonvertex angles of a kite are _____.

7. The diagonals of a kite are _____.

8. The consecutive angles between the bases of a trapezoid are _____.

9. The midsegment of a triangle is _____ times the length of the base.

10. The midsegment of a trapezoid is the _____ of the lengths of the bases.

11. A rhombus is a(n) _____ with perpendicular diagonals.

12. A square is a(n) _____ with congruent sides.

13. If a trapezoid has congruent base angles, it is _____.

Review Questions

Chapter 6: Polygon Properties

For problems 14–19, answer each question and find the best answer on your Matho board. You may want to sketch a picture first.

14. The midsegment of a trapezoid measures 3 cm. Find the length (in cm) of one base if the other base measures 4.2 cm.

15. A student cuts a polygon along two lines and forms three congruent equilateral triangles. What shape was the original polygon?

16. A student reflects a triangle across one of its sides. What quadrilateral consists of the original triangle plus the image triangle?

17. A kite has angles of 80° and 130°. Find another one of its angles.

18. An exterior angle of a regular polygon is 30°. Find the number of sides of the polygon.

19. Describe polygon *ABCD*, if *A* has coordinates (2, 1), *B* has coordinates (1, 2), *C* has coordinates (4, 5), and *D* has coordinates (4, 3).

Review Questions

Chapter 6: Polygon Properties

In problems 20–24, find the measures of the following angles in the diagram.

20. *a*   **21.** *b*   **22.** *c*   **23.** *d*   **24.** *e*

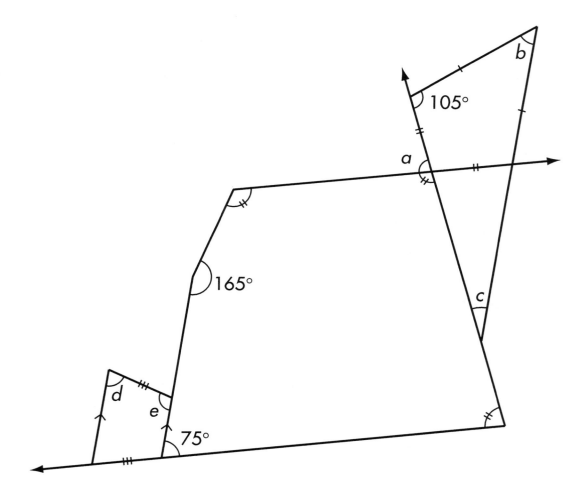

Review Answer Sheet

Chapter 6

rhombus	perpendicular	rectangle
hexagon	supplementary	75°
congruent	average	1.8	20°
parallelogram	12	80°
isosceles	trapezoid	50°	25°
trapezoid	135°	540°	0.5
kite	isosceles	360°	105°

Folding Paper Circles

Sharon Grand

Teacher Notes

You can use this exercise in several ways: as a midunit review activity for Chapter 7, as a review activity after completing all of Chapter 7, or as an informal assessment at the end of the chapter. It can also serve as an early introduction to justification and proof. The activity introduces the tetrahedron in step 8 and the truncated tetrahedron in step 9, so you can use it as a springboard for further study of Platonic and Archimedean solids. Once they are completed, students can use their folded circles for reference when they study similar figures. (Or you could repeat the paper folding as a quick review.) This works especially well if students begin with circles of different sizes.

It's probably simplest to give students these directions orally.

Prerequisites

Students need to be familiar with the following conjectures. This exercise will serve to review them.

- The measure of an angle inscribed in a circle is half the measure of its intercepted arc.

- In a circle, congruent chords are equidistant from the center and intercept congruent arcs.

- The midsegment of a triangle is parallel to the third side and one half its length.

Materials Needed

Large paper circles (you can have students make these using blank paper, a compass, and a pair of scissors).

Folding Paper Circles

Sharon Grand

Use the steps below to fold a circle.

1. Cut a large circle from a piece of unlined paper. Mark the center.

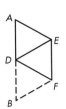

2. Fold a point of the circle to the center. Call the crease segment *AB*. How far from the center is the chord? Identify the major and minor arcs for chord *AB*.

3. Use *B* as an endpoint of a second crease. Fold a second point of the circle to the center (segment *BC*). How far from the center is the chord? Identify the major and minor arcs for chord *BC*. What is true about the lengths of the chords *AB* and *BC*?

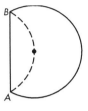

4. Fold segment *AC*. What kind of triangle is *ABC*? How do you know? Compare the three minor arcs. What are their measures? Compare the measures of the angles of the triangles to the measures of the arcs.

5. Locate the midpoint of segment *AB* (point *D*). Fold point *C* to point *D*. Crease to form segment *EF*. What kind of quadrilateral is *ABFE*? Explain how you know this.

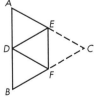

6. Fold *B* across to point *E* along segment *DF*. Identify *ADFE*. Explain how you know this.

7. Fold point *A* across to point *F* along segment *DE*. What type of triangle did you form? How do you know? How does it compare to the first triangle? Unfold and compare the areas of the two triangles.

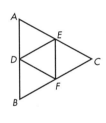

8. Open back to triangle *ABC*. Form a three-dimensional solid by folding along *DE, EF,* and *DF*. Discuss the three-dimensional shape that you formed.

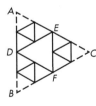

9. Fold point A to the midpoint of *DE*, point *B* to the mid-point of *DF,* and point *C* to the mid-point of *EF*. Slip the smallest triangle flaps (points *A, B,* and *C*) inside each other to make a truncated tetrahedron.

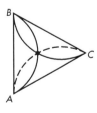

10. Unfold to the original circle. Discuss the geometric concepts/ figures shown within the folded lines. Decorate your final product colorfully to show a particular geometric property.

Symmetry in Snowflakes

Sharon Grand

Teacher Notes

Many students remember creating paper snowflakes when they were in elementary school, to decorate their classroom windows and to give as gifts. This project allows them to enjoy that process again while incorporating the geometry concepts and vocabulary they have been using in the mathematics class, especially the idea of symmetry and the relationships between angle measures and polygon shapes. It is also an object lesson on the importance of listening to and writing instructions, and can foster cooperation among students as they share their understanding and creative ideas. In addition, this project is another way for students to link art and creativity to mathematics so they become more aware of this influence in the world around them.

Time Required

One day for in-class demonstration and project assignment

Two to five days for students to complete a project outside of class

One day for class "show and tell" (optional)

Materials

- Scissors for each student

- Four sheets of typing paper (or newsprint) for each student

- Three to six pieces cut from sheets of tissue paper for each student

- Trash can or trash bag for each group

- Protractor for each student

- Laminating machine with laminating film

Teacher Preparation

1. Purchase packages of colored or decorative tissue paper; this usually comes with about 10 sheets per package, with each sheet measuring about 24 in. by 36 in. Using a paper cutter or scissors, cut all 10 sheets into rectangles approximately 9 in. by 12 in. Don't worry about cutting exactly, because the folding takes care of cutting errors.

2. Following the directions for folding, make patterns for each type of polygon from pieces of newsprint or plain paper. Mark the first fold with a "1" next to the fold, the second fold with a "2," and so on so that you will have a handy guide to use when demonstrating for your students. Do not cut along the cut lines of your patterns, but mark them so you can tell the students where to cut. Be sure to label each pattern with the type of polygon it produces.

3. Following your folding pattern for each type of polygon, cut snowflakes from tissue paper and laminate them to show as examples for your students.

Instructions

1. Making the patterns: Students should use the plain paper or newsprint to make folding patterns like the ones the teacher made for demonstration purposes. They should make and number the creases, add notes to make the pattern more clear to follow, mark the cut lines, and label the type of polygon each produces.

   a. Lead students through the folds for a pentagon, but don't tell them what shape will result. Stress the geometry vocabulary while folding, using *bisect, right angle,* and so on. Have the students measure the smallest angle of the resulting triangle and record the results; ask them to predict what shape will result from opening up the triangle. The teacher should actually cut the paper, but the students need to save their papers to use as patterns. Open the paper and ask questions as to what shape it is; what the angle measures should be; the relationship between the measured angle, the resulting central angle, and the number of sides; what types of symmetry there are; and so on.

   b. Using additional sheets of paper, lead the students through the folding patterns for a hexagon and an octagon, using vocabulary and questions as above. Ask the students to predict what polygon will result from the folds, then make the cut to verify their predictions. They should give reasons for their predictions.

   c. Have the students follow their own patterns to fold the hexagon. This time, they should cut along the cut line, but they should not open the paper yet. Tell them to cut out designs along any of the folds, the outside edges, and/or the center. After they've had several minutes to cut, they should open up the pieces of paper to see the "snowflakes" they have created. The teacher should do this also. Tell the students that the more they cut away, the lacier their snowflakes will be.

2. Completing the project: The students will use the tissue paper to create a snowflake based on each of the three polygons demonstrated; this will be done outside of class and turned in approximately one week (or less) after the instructions are given. They may use their own tissue or gift-wrap paper, and they may decorate their snowflakes with sequins, glitter, or other materials. The snowflakes should be flattened by pressing them between heavy books a night or two before they are due.

Use a large folder or piece of poster board to collect the snowflakes and keep them flat. They can then be laminated by using a laminating machine with rolls of film or by using a laminating press; even delicate snowflakes can be laminated if they've been pressed flat. Lamination not only makes them durable for display purposes, but also enhances their appearance. The students can now share their designs with the class, write journal entries about the geometric concepts illustrated, and make a classroom display on the bulletin boards or in the windows.

Symmetry in Snowflakes

Sharon Grand

Folding Instructions for a Pentagon

1. Begin with paper in horizontal position.

2. Fold in half with vertical crease *EF,* bringing left edge *AD* over to right edge *BC*.

3. Fold *F* to *A* and make a small crease marking the midpoint of *FA* (point *G*). Open the paper back up to step 2.

4. Fold *E* to *G* and make crease *HJ*.

5. Match *HJ* on top of *HE* and make crease *HK*. This crease should bisect ∠*JHE*.

6. Fold the △*HFG* flap backward, under the paper, using crease *HJ* as your guideline to fold along. When you make crease *HG*, you will also bisect ∠*KHF*.

7. Flip over by rotating about point *H*. Cut along *FG*.

8. Keep △*HFG*. If you open it now, you will get a pentagon. If you want to make a snowflake, cut along the edges before opening.

Folding Instructions for a Hexagon

1. Begin with paper in horizontal position.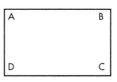

2. Fold in half with vertical crease *EF,* bringing left edge *AD* over to right edge *BC*.

3. Fold in half with horizontal crease *GH*.

4. Fold in half again with horizontal crease *JK*.

5. Unfold it once.

6. Place lower left corner *E/F* on crease *JK* so you can make a crease through upper-right corner *G*. Make crease *GM*.

7. Bisect ∠*MGH* by folding under, using crease GF as your folding guide.

8. Cut along *FM*. Keep △*GFM*. If you open it now, you will get a hexagon. If you want to make a snowflake, cut along the edges before opening.

Folding Instructions for an Octagon

1. Begin with paper in vertical position.

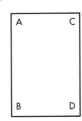

2. Fold in half with horizontal crease *EF*, bringing top edge *AC* down to bottom edge *BD*.

3. Fold in half with vertical crease *GH*.

4. Bisect ∠*EGH* by placing upper left corner *E/F* on crease *GH* and making a crease through upper-left corner *G*. The new crease is *GJ*.

5. Bisect ∠*JGF* by placing edge *GF* on top of edge *GJ* and making a crease through point *G*. This crease is *GK*.

6. Bisect ∠*JGH* by folding under, using *GK* as your folding guide.

7. Cut along *EK*. Keep Δ*GEK*. If you open it now, you will get an octagon. If you want to make a snowflake, cut along the edges before opening.

Tessellation T-shirts

Carolyn Sessions

Teacher Notes

This process can be used to transfer a tessellation to a T-shirt or any piece of fabric. The best kind of T-shirt to use is a 50/50 cotton-polyester blend rather than a shirt made of 100 percent cotton. If your students can't afford T-shirts, buy white muslin from a discount store and cut it into squares. Students can transfer their tessellations to the squares, and you can make a class quilt by using tape or fusible hem tape to hold the squares together.

Materials

- Fabric crayons (available at school supply, arts and crafts, and some fabric stores)

- Tracing paper (Patty paper has a finish that comes off on the shirt when heated. Avoid using patty paper for this project.)

- Iron and ironing board

- Large sheets of clean, white paper (sheets from an artist's sketchpad works well, but any white, nonwaxed paper should work). Blank newsprint also works.

1. Ask students to draw a design that will tessellate onto a sheet of white paper. Then have students use a pencil to tessellate their design onto a sheet of tracing paper so that the tessellation covers the entire sheet of paper. Students must trace the outline and details for each design tile.

2. Once the tessellation has been traced onto the tracing paper, students can use fabric crayons to color the back side of the paper. Make sure they don't color the side on which the tessellation has been traced. Some students also like to color a single design tile for the shirt's front pocket area.

3. Set the iron to its hottest setting and place the shirt on the ironing board. Put a sheet of clean white paper inside the shirt, between the front and the back, so that the colors don't bleed through both sides of the shirt.

4. Smooth wrinkles from the shirt. Center the tessellation on the front or the back of the shirt, about 2 inches below the neckline. Make sure the colored side of the tessellation is next to the fabric.

5. Cover the tessellation with a clean sheet of white paper. Iron on the white paper, pressing lightly and making sure to iron over all the edges. If you find that the iron is starting to scorch the fabric, use a lower temperature setting or more white paper as protective thickness.

6. To check for a complete transfer, anchor the center of the white paper and the tracing paper with one finger. Carefully lift the edges of both pieces of paper. If not all parts of the tessellation are evenly transferred, reposition it carefully and iron again over the lightly transferred areas. Again, watch for scorching.

Tessellation T-shirts

Carolyn Sessions

In this project you will transfer your own tessellation to a T-shirt or a piece of fabric. (The best kind of T-shirt to use is a 50/50 cotton-polyester blend rather than a shirt made of 100 percent cotton.) Follow the steps below to create your tessellation.

1. Look through Chapter 8 of *Discovering Geometry* and use one of the methods described to make your own design to tessellate. Include detail in your design.

2. On tracing paper, use a pencil to carefully tessellate your design so that the tessellation covers the entire sheet of paper. Be sure to trace your design's detail, too. Leave room for the title of your tessellation and your signature (see steps 3 and 4 below).

3. Title your tessellation and write the title on the tracing paper where you think it will look best. Make your letters large enough to be seen from a distance. ("Bubble" letters look nice.)

4. Sign your tessellation with your name. If you have a "famous" signature, use it. You may want to make your signature a little larger than you normally would.

5. Bring your masterpiece to school so you can transfer it to your shirt.

Follow the steps below to prepare your tessellation for transfer onto your T-shirt or piece of fabric.

1. On the *back* of your tracing paper, draw over the outline of your tessellation with a dark-colored fabric crayon. Then color the interior of the tessellation.

2. Outline and color your title.

3. Outline your signature with a dark-colored crayon.

4. If you want a design on your shirt's front pocket area, use a small sheet of tracing paper to trace, outline, and color a single design tile. Remember, color the back of the traced design tile.

5. Ask your teacher or an assigned "peer helper" to help you transfer your tessellation to your T-shirt.

Building a Home

Ralph Bothe

When architects and builders work with a client, they must do a careful analysis to estimate costs of renovating an existing home or building a new home or office. Based on the information in the blueprints, they calculate the areas of all of the rooms, walls, and ceilings to determine the amounts and costs of things such as paint, carpet, tile, and sheetrock. They use these calculations to estimate the amount of money their client will have to pay to complete a job. The challenge is to keep costs low enough to satisfy the client and choose materials that look nice and last. For this project, you will determine costs to do some of the jobs required to finish building a home.

Using the floor plan included with this project, estimate the costs to do the following.

1. Carpet the three bedrooms. (Don't forget about the carpet pad.)

2. Put in hardwood floors for the living room and dining room.

3. Sheetrock the garage walls and ceiling. (Assume a 10-ft ceiling.)

4. Tile the bathroom and front entry.

5. Paint the living room and dining room. (Assume a 12-ft ceiling)

6. Put baseboard in all rooms that are measured in the floor plan.

For each job that you are writing up a cost estimate for, you will need to do the following.

1. Research the product you need. Find out what sizes it comes in and how you buy it. List the names of at least two suppliers that sell the product. If possible, obtain literature about the product showing samples, colors, and types. Choose a particular product to use.

2. Calculate the quantity needed. Show all calculations in detail and show how you arrived at the quantity needed. Explain how you would order it from the supplier.

3. Obtain at least two bids for the job to be done. Get bids with and without labor. Find out if there are different levels of quality for the product and why you might want a certain level of quality.

4. Select one of the bids and explain why you picked that bid.

5. Write up a clear itemized cost estimate for each job as if you were a contractor bidding the job for a client. You may want to include an alternate choice, with an explanation of the possible benefits of choosing one option over the other. In addition, include the sample materials, detailed calculations, and final cost with and without labor.

Extensions

Try this project using the floor plan for your own home, find plans in an architectural magazine or book, or, if you are ambitious, draw your own scale floor plan of your dream home.

Building a Home

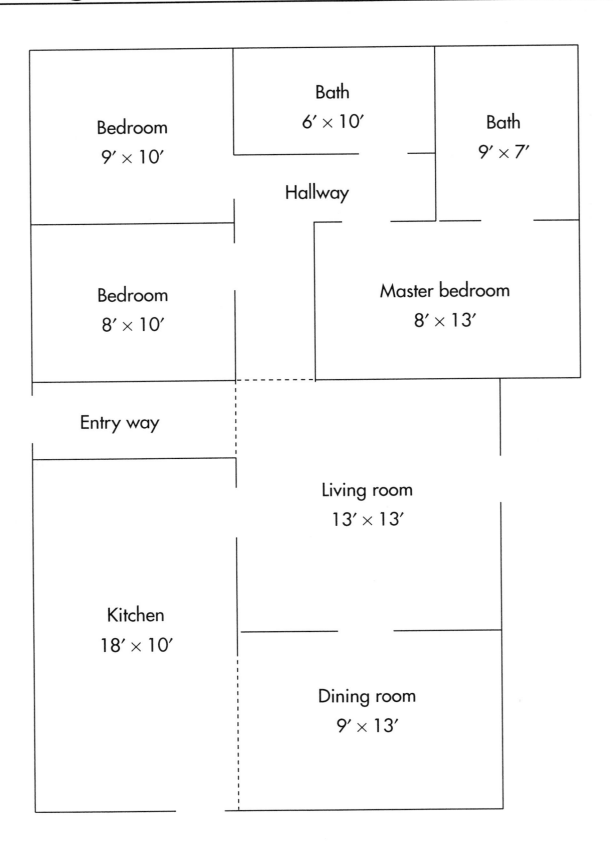

Bedroom
9′ × 10′

Bath
6′ × 10′

Bath
9′ × 7′

Hallway

Bedroom
8′ × 10′

Master bedroom
8′ × 13′

Entry way

Living room
13′ × 13′

Kitchen
18′ × 10′

Dining room
9′ × 13′

Finding Another Proof of the Pythagorean Theorem

Masha Albrecht

Many different people have found original proofs of the Pythagorean Theorem. Historical documents show ancient proofs of this famous theorem by mathematicians from all over the world. Modern mathematicians, a U.S. president, and even some high school students have found unique proofs of the theorem in more recent times.

The first task in this project is to find a proof of this theorem that you have not already studied in class. Then you must learn enough about this particular proof to write a report or make a poster. These are the requirements for the project:

- Your project must contain an explanation of the proof that makes sense to you and your classmates.

  This is the hardest part of the project, because many of the proofs are complicated. Here are some steps to help.

  1. First make sure you understand the proof yourself. If you need another person to help you make sense of it, ask a friend, a group member, a relative, or a teacher.
  2. Decide what kind of presentation would make the proof simplest to understand. Would it be clearer on a poster? Would it help to make a dynamic geometry sketch using a geometry software program?
  3. Create a first draft of your explanation and have a friend, group member, or relative read it over. Find someone who has about as much math knowledge as you and your classmates. If they do not understand parts of it, improve on these parts to make them clearer.

- Your project must contain a description of the discoverer of the proof. Try to include interesting facts about the person's life. How did he or she come up with the proof?

- Your project must contain a list of resources.

  Explain where you found the proof and include the name of anyone who helped you.

  Here are some suggestions for places to look for resources:

  1. Look in your school library or local library.
  2. Look on the World Wide Web.
  3. Ask math teachers if they have any books you can look through. Even a different geometry textbook can be a good resource.

- Your project should be colorful. Make sure you include lots of drawings, since these can make the project easier to read and understand.

Packing Efficiency and Displacement
Carolyn Sessions

The purpose of this exercise is to have you try displacement to determine how efficient the packaging is for items we buy each day.

Materials

- One sheet of poster paper

- One tube of toothpaste and the box that it came in

- One light bulb and the box that it came in

- Graduated cylinder or container large enough to measure the volume of the light bulb and toothpaste tube

- Water

You are to submit a *single* poster that demonstrates how to determine each of the following:

1. Use displacement to find the volume of a tube of toothpaste and the light bulb. Save the cardboard box and the corrugated package that the toothpaste and the light bulb came in.

   a. Sketch a picture of the container and the water level before the object is submerged. Write in all dimensions.

   b. Sketch a picture of the container and the water level after the object is submerged.

   c. Show the calculations used from parts a. and b. to determine the volumes of the toothpaste and the light bulb.

   d. Attach the toothpaste tube and light bulb to your poster.

2. Attach the packages that the toothpaste and the light bulb came in to the poster paper. Label the dimensions of each box. Find the volume of each box, showing the steps needed for the calculations.

3. Determine the number of cubic cm of air space that would be inside the box when the object is packaged. (How much air space is in the package containing the tube of toothpaste or light bulb when the toothpaste tube or light bulb is put in the box?)

4. Calculate the percentage of air space in the box by using the following formula:

   % air space = volume of air/volume of packaging container.

5. Determine which packaging container is most efficient.

Notes

   a. All measurements should be made to the nearest tenth of a centimeter.

   b. Information showing how to do displacement can be found in Lesson 11.6 of *Discovering Geometry.*

   c. Make sure that you find a container that will be easy to determine the volume of the water in the container. A rectangular prism is usually best. A waxed cardboard half-gallon milk container that has a square base is probably best.

Similarity in Grow Creatures

Carolyn Sessions

Teacher Notes

Students will use their knowledge of similar figures to determine whether two three-dimensional figures are similar. One version of this project also allows for the collection and analysis of data over time and for the use of graphing calculators, if available.

Materials

- One Grow Creature per group (see note on Grow Creatures below)
- One large sealable plastic bag per group
- One flat growing pan per group
- Tape measures and/or rulers
- Balance beams
- Graduated cylinders or other containers that can be used to find volume by displacement (optional)
- Graphing calculators or spreadsheet package (optional, but helpful on growth pattern version of this project)

What are Grow Creatures and how do I get them?

Grow Creatures are toys that expand when placed in water. They come in different shapes, but the best ones to use for this project are called Grow SeaLife and Grow Brains. There are also Grow Beasts, Grow Roaches, and Grow Bats, but they are too small or too light to easily calculate their original volumes, so leave out the volume component if you choose these creatures. The Grow Roaches are probably the most realistic looking and their growth is amazing.

Grow Creatures can be purchased retail or wholesale. The wholesaler for Grow Creatures is Accoutrements in Seattle, Washington (1-800-886-2221), who require a minimum order of $100. Accoutrements can give you the name of the nearest retailer if you want to buy in smaller quantities. You will pay more to buy retail, but you can buy in smaller quantities.

Procedure

1. Determine which of the two instruction sets best fits your needs. The set labeled Grow Creatures Growth Patterns involves analyzing growth over time and tests for similarity. The set labeled Similarity in Grow Creatures focuses on using the rules of similarity without the need to graph data over time.

2. Introduce the project by finding a Grow Creature whose package indicates a given percent of growth. (Grow Beasts (dinosaurs) have had this labeling in the past.) Ask students what they think this advertisement means. Discuss with the students whether or not they think the grown creature will look like the original. Review the characteristics of two similar three-dimensional figures if necessary.

3. Allow students to follow the steps listed in the project. Students may need some help in finding a way to measure the heights of their creatures. Suggest using a stiff index card and placing it so that it lies parallel to another flat surface (such as a desktop) and measuring the distance between the two planes. Note: Tape measures work well for length and width, but plastic or wooden rulers work best for the height measurements.

Similarity in Grow Creatures

Carolyn Sessions

The packaging for Grow Beasts and Grow Creatures sometimes indicates that the creature will grow 600%. To what does this refer? Is a grown creature similar to the original? What relationships exist between the two creatures? We will take some linear measurements and also measure the mass and volume of the creature.

1. What kind of creature do you have? Give it a name.

2. Take your creature and trace its outline on a sheet of unlined paper.

3. Measure the length, width, and depth (height) of your creature. Record these measurements in the data chart. To remember the locations at which you took these measurements, go to the outline that you traced earlier and mark the places where the measurements were made. This will help you with later measurements.

Grow Creature Data Chart

	Length	Width	Depth	Volume	Mass
Original					
Grown					

4. Use one of the triple-beam balances to measure the mass of your creature. Record the data on your data sheet.

5. Use displacement to measure the volume of your creature in cubic cm. Record the data on your data sheet.

6. Place your creature in your growing pan (or sealable plastic bag) and cover it with water. You should have the water level about 1/2 in. higher than the creature.

7. Now it's time to let your creature grow. . . .

After the Growing Process:

8. Measure the dimensions of the creature in the same locations where measurements were taken earlier. Record your measurements in the Grow Creature data chart that you used in step 3.

9. Find the volume and mass of your creature. Make a drawing, label dimensions needed to find the volume, and calculate the volume.

10. What is the ratio of the volume of your original figure to the enlarged creature?

11. Did your creature grow proportionally? Use mathematics to justify your answer.

12. Lightly squeeze some of the water from your creature. Place the creature in a safe place to dry. Each day you should record measurements until your creature has reached its original size (or very close to it). If there aren't enough blanks in the chart below, you may add more.

	Length	Width	Height
Day 1			
Day 2			
Day 3			
Day 4			

13. Okay, now you have watched your creature grow and recorded a lot of data. Now what? Write a 1.5- to 2-page summary of the project. You should use the data sheets above as a guide for information, but do not just rewrite all the information. As a part of this summary, reflect on your ideas about similar figures and volume before beginning this project. How did this project alter those ideas? Did the project help your understanding of proportional growth and volume? Explain. In your paper, describe the drying process. Did you see any patterns? Use your notes to help with this section. What are the relationships between the manner in which the grow creature dried and the way humans are affected by cold and heat?

Do the best job you can on this paper. Make sure you use correct grammar and punctuation; use your best organizational skills. Also, use good mathematical skills in your analysis. Be sure your paper reflects your understanding of the principles being studied. Your paper should be typed and double spaced.

Grow Creatures Growth Patterns

Carolyn Sessions

The packaging for Grow Beasts and Grow Creatures sometimes indicates that the creature will grow 600%. To what does this refer? Is a grown creature similar to the original? What relationships exist between the two creatures?

In order to complete this exercise, we must make some measurements prior to and during the growth process of our creatures. We will take some linear measurements and also measure the mass and volume of the creature.

1. What kind of creature do you have? Give it a name. _____

2. Take your creature and trace its outline on a sheet of unlined paper.

3. Measure the length, width, and depth (height) of your creature. Record these measurements on the attached data sheet. To remember the locations at which you took these measurements, go to the outline that you traced earlier and mark the places where the measurements were made. This will help you with later measurements.

4. Use one of the triple-beam balances to measure the mass of your creature. Record the data on your data sheet.

5. Use displacement to measure the volume of your creature in cubic cm. Record the data on your data sheet.

6. Place your creature in your growing pan (or sealable plastic bag) and cover it with water. You should have the water level about 1/2 in. higher than the creature.

7. Now it's time to let your creature grow, but we want to make some measurements during the growing process. Someone in your group is going to adopt your pet for the evening. Take it home and make two more measurements today—one this afternoon and one tonight before you go to bed. Also try to make a measurement before you come to school (or you can come to my room before school starts in the morning to make your morning measurement and to drop your creature off until class). We will repeat this process tomorrow. Record your data on the Grow Creature Data Sheet.

Data Analysis

1. In your group, divide up the linear data. Each person is to graph time vs. some dimension. (Person 1 can graph time vs. length; Person 2, time vs. width, and so on, on your graphing calculator.) Does the data look linear? Try to find the equation that is a good "fit" for your data. This equation is called the "model" of the physical data.

2. Compare the results of the graph you made for question 1 with those of others who graphed time vs. another measurement. Is your grown creature similar to the original? How can you tell?

3. Find the ratio of the mass of the grown creature to that of the original. Find the ratio of the volume of the grown creature to that of the original. Are there any relationships here? Should there be?

4. Find the ratios of the length measurement of the grown creature to the original length measurement; the ratio of the widths; the ratio of the depths. What does this information tell you about the growth of the creature?

5. Compare the ratios of the linear measurements to the ratios of the masses and volumes. What relationships appear here?

Project

Write a conclusion or summary about the growing process and data analysis that you did with your creature. Your objective is to discuss the physical meaning of the model you created. You might want to consider similarity and the limits of the problem. What does this problem say about the physical properties of the Grow Creature? Remember, you should not simply restate the steps that you used in this lab; you are trying to summarize what you found, relate it to the features of the grown creature and the original, and show how your findings are related to the advertisement on the package.

Grow Creatures Growth Patterns

Grow Creature Data Sheet

Start Date and Time: _____

Measurement	Number Hours	Length	Width	Depth	Volume	Mass	Number	Growing Time
1.								
2.								
3.								
4.								
5.								
6.								
7.								
8.								
9.								
10.								
11.								
12.								

Note: The more measurements you can make, the better.

The Geometry of Baseball

Carolyn Sessions

The following facts are related to baseball. There are many geometric concepts involved. You and your group should answer each of the questions in detail, using as many geometry principles as possible to justify your answers.

Location of the Pitcher

A baseball diamond is officially defined as a 90-ft square. The pitcher throws the ball to the batter from a position 60 ft 6 in. away from home plate.

1. Is the pitcher's position in front of, on, or behind the line from first to third base? Draw a diagram and use mathematics to justify your answer.

Laying Out the Bases

According to the 1992 official handbook, when laying out the field, "when the location of home plate is determined, use a steel tape to measure 127 feet, 3-3/8 inches in the desired direction to establish second base. From home plate measure 90 feet towards first base. From second base measure 90 feet towards first base. The intersection of these lines locates first base."

Discuss or write up answers to the following questions:

2. Is the official method used to locate first base correct?

3. Is it reasonable?

4. Why do you think the rules specify the distances as they do?

5. Describe a technique that could be used to execute the instructions.

6. Are the lines connecting first to second and first to home perpendicular?

Pitching Speed

7. If the pitcher throws the ball at 90 mph, how long does it take the ball to reach home plate? How long for a 60-mph pitcher?

Where to Stand in the Batter's Box

The batter's box extends 3 ft behind and 3 ft in front of the center of the rubber for home plate. Sometimes coaches advise batters to stand at the back of the batter's box when facing exceptionally fast pitchers. Why?

For a 90-mph pitch, how much longer does it take the ball to get to a batter standing at the back of the batter's box than it does to get to a batter standing in front of the box? Do the same calculation for a 70-mph pitch. Assess the advantage of standing as far as possible from the pitcher. Does this position have any disadvantages?

8. Write up an explanation.

A Möbius Strip: The Surface with a Twist

Luis Shein

You've seen and used many surfaces both inside and outside your geometry class. Some surfaces are flat like a plane, some are curved like a sphere, some have edges like a polygon, and some go on forever. In this project, you will create a simple surface with some surprising features called a Möbius strip.

Materials

- Paper
- Scissors
- Tape

Part 1

The Möbius Strip

1. The artist M. C. Escher, like many people, was fascinated with the geometry of the Möbius strip. Look at his picture *Möbius Strip II,* on page 677 of your *Discovering Geometry* textbook. Pick a starting place and follow the path of the ants. Start with one ant, move forward to the next ant, and so on. Keep following the ants until you return to the starting place. (Hint: It is easier to follow this ladder-like path if you trace along the edge with your finger.) Write a paragraph that describes any surprising features you noticed about this path.

2. Cut two strips of paper that are about 1 by 12 inches. It would be best if you use paper that is a different color on each side. If you have only plain white paper, color one side of each strip.

   Draw arrows on one strip like this:

   Strip 1

   Tape together the ends of the first strip so that both arrows point in the same direction. Briefly describe the surface you have created. Include a sketch of the surface with your description.

3. Draw arrows on the second strip like this:

   Strip 2

   Tape together the ends of the second strip so that both arrows point in the same direction. You have just created a Möbius strip. Before you describe your Möbius strip, try these few simple activities:

   a. Take your pencil and draw a path along the Möbius strip similar to the one traveled by the ants. Don't lift your pencil until you return to your starting place.

b. Your original strip of paper was colored differently on different sides. Inspect the coloring of your Möbius strip.

c. Imagine that you are painting surfaces, with the rule that the front and back of a surface must be different colors. How many colors will you need for the first surface you made? How many will you need for the Möbius strip?

Now describe the Möbius strip you have created. A good description would include:

• A sketch of the surface (colors would be helpful)

• Descriptions of your results from a., b., and c., above

• Further comparisons of the Möbius strip with the simpler surface you created first

4. Belts that drive motors and fans are often shaped like Möbius strips. Explain why these belts last approximately twice as long as a regular cylindrically shaped belt.

5. Open up your own Möbius strip to turn it back into a two-dimensional strip again. Inspect the path you drew with your pencil. The path was closed because your pencil returned to the same place where it started. Notice that the penciled path appears on both sides of the strip.

Since most surfaces we read from, write on, and draw on are two-dimensional, it's helpful to be able to represent the Möbius strip in two dimensions. It's also helpful if this representation uses only one side of the page. One way to do this is to use a flat rectangle, somewhat like your original strip of paper. Pretend the left-hand side of the rectangle is actually connected to the right-hand side, and that the rectangle has a twist.

Imagine a number line from 0 to 1 on either side of the strip, like those in the picture above. In order to represent the twisted connection, the number lines appear to have opposite orientations. Point 0 on one corner maps to point 0 on the opposite corner. Likewise, 1 maps to 1, 1/2 maps to 1/2, 1/10 maps to 1/10, and so on. In this representation, you do not need to use the back of the rectangle. Also, the actual length and width of the rectangle are not very important.

Any path you can draw on the rectangle that starts and ends at the same number actually forms a closed path. For example, in the diagram, the path that starts at 1/10 and ends at 1/10 is a closed path.

Use this method to draw a representation of the penciled path from your Möbius strip on a flat sheet of paper. Explain how the actual path on your flattened Möbius strip appears differently from the one in your representation. Describe any advantages and disadvantages you see in this rectangular representation of a Möbius strip.

Part 2

Cutting the Möbius Strip

1. a. The diagram below shows a two-dimensional representation of the simpler cylindrical surface you made first (the one without the twist). Try to imagine cutting a path on the cylindrical band from the midpoint of one side to the midpoint of the second side. Predict what will happen when you cut your cylindrical band along this line.

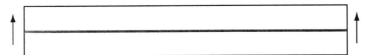

   b. Now go ahead and cut your cylindrical band right down the middle. Describe your results. Was your prediction correct?

2. a. Imagine doing the same thing on the Möbius strip. What do you think will happen to your strip if you cut it along a path that joins the midpoints of both sides in the diagram below? Think hard before you make this prediction. If you predict this one right, you have excellent visualization skills!

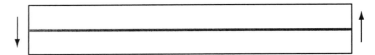

   b. Now go ahead and cut your Möbius strip down the middle. (You may need to tape it back together again first.) Describe your results. Is this what you expected?

3. For a truly unusual experience, cut your already-cut Möbius strip again. If you are brave, you can try to predict the results before you actually do this. Record your results and any surprises you have.

Research Ideas

- Search for Möbius strips in use. Ask a mechanic or consult a car repair manual.

- Find out where the name Möbius came from.

- Find games and simulations that use Möbius strips for their surfaces. You could also design one yourself.

- If you are interested in a surface even stranger than the Möbius strip, learn about the Klein bottle.

Writing a Logic Puzzle

Eberhard Scheiffele

In Chapter 14, you studied the basic principles of logic. You can apply these principles to write puzzles whose solutions depend mainly on a correct application of logic (deductive reasoning). Consider the following example:

The theft was committed by Rose, Charles, or Steve. If Charles had committed the theft, Holmes would know about it. Neither Holmes nor Watson knows who committed the theft. If Steve did not commit the theft, Rose is innocent.

The information in this puzzle is sufficient to tell you who committed the theft. You only need to apply logic. You don't have to know anything else about the suspects. The best way to think about it is to realize that to assume Charles or Rose committed the theft leads to a contradiction. If Charles had committed the theft, Holmes would know about it. But you also know that neither Holmes nor Watson knows who committed the theft. This is a contradiction, so it is impossible that Charles is the criminal. If Rose had committed the theft, then by *modus tollens* you would know it is not true that Steve did not commit the theft. This would mean that both Steve and Rose are the criminals. This is a contradiction to the first statement that *one* of the three—Rose, Charles, or Steve—committed the theft. The last remaining choice is that the thief is Steve. Now you should, of course, make sure that assuming Steve committed the theft does not lead to a contradiction.

Some people find it useful to translate the given information into symbolic form. If we use T for "is the thief" and K for "knows who committed the theft" (and R for Rose, and so on), we can write the given information in the example as:

1. T(R) or T(C) or T(S)

2. T(C) → K(H)

3. Neither K(H) nor K(W) [This is equivalent to ~K(H) and ~K(W).]

4. ~T(S) → ~T(R)

Logic alone allows you to conclude that T(S) is true and hence Steve is the thief. The proof is an indirect proof: "Assume the opposite of the conclusion, ~T(S). Then by (4) we have ~T(R). Then by (1) we conclude T(C). Then by (2) we get K(H). But by (3) we have ~K(H), which is a contradiction."

Now try to solve the following puzzle:

The students are talking during lunch. They are discussing the adventures of Barbara, Isabelle, Marguerite, and Yuschka. The teacher, who listened for a while, asks them, "Who are you talking about?" The oldest of the students answers: "We are talking about a girl, a cat, a dog, and a mouse." The teacher replies, "But who is what?" The students want to challenge the teacher and answer, "If Yuschka is not the mouse and Isabelle is not the girl, Marguerite is the dog. If Barbara is not the cat, then, if Yuschka is not the girl, Isabelle is the dog. At least one of the three following statements is correct: Marguerite is the cat, Barbara is the mouse, Yuschka is the dog. If neither Marguerite nor Barbara is the girl, Isabelle is the dog."

"Stop! That's enough for me to know who is what," the teacher interrupts.

See if you can figure out who is the girl, the cat, the dog, and the mouse.

Challenge for extra credit: Can you prove that your answer is the only possible correct answer?

Here is a sketch showing how you can make up similar puzzles:

Make up a story in which you use names of persons, animals, or things. It's best to start with a specific assignment of the names to the objects in mind. Let's say, for example, you want to make up a story about your hamster Rudi, your snake Till, and your turtle Joel. Now you have to make up sentences with logical connectives (and, or, if-then, not, and so on) that are true under your assignment of names to objects. Obviously it would be too easy to just use: "Rudi is the hamster, Till is the snake, and Joel is the turtle." So you might try (1) "If Joel is not the hamster, Till is the snake."

Always check to make sure your sentence is true. You need to create sentences that are false under some of the other possibilities (of assignments). For example, the sentence (2) "Joel is not the hamster or Till is the snake" excludes all assignments in which Joel is the hamster and Till is not the snake.

When you have enough sentences, such that all the other possibilities are excluded, you are finished. For example, if you add (3) "Joel is the turtle or Rudi is the snake," then sentences (1)–(3) imply that Joel is the turtle. Why? Check that assuming Rudi is the snake leads to a contradiction. But then (1) implies that Till is the snake. Then of course Rudi has to be the hamster. So the sentences (1)–(3) allow only one solution.

Now make up your own puzzle and exchange it with another student. Don't forget to keep a note with the correct solution. It's easiest to start with only two different names and then make up more difficult puzzles later. You may even want to put in some additional statements that are not pertinent to the solution to make it more difficult to solve.

Proof by Mathematical Induction

Eberhard Scheiffele and Masha Albrecht

Mathematical induction is a special procedure you can use to prove that a property holds true for an infinite sequence of events. The procedure involves two steps. Before you see a precise mathematical example, let's look at some other representations. These will help you make sense of this two-step process.

Example 1

Suppose you need to climb a ladder with infinitely many rungs. You want to be sure you eventually get to every rung. In order to be sure of this, you need to satisfy both these conditions:

I. You are sure you can climb onto the first rung of the ladder.

II. Every time you are on a rung of the ladder, you are sure you can get to the next rung.

Can you see how these two conditions guarantee that you can climb the ladder forever?

Example 2

Have you ever made a chain of dominoes? If you haven't ever made a domino chain, find someone who can describe one to you. Now imagine a domino chain that goes on forever and uses infinitely many dominoes. You plan to knock down this domino chain, but you want to be sure that you can knock over every single domino. One way to be sure is to satisfy both these conditions:

I. You are sure you can knock over the first domino.

II. Every time a domino falls over, you are sure it will knock over the next one too.

In step I in each example, you need to show that a condition holds for the first possible case. In step II, you need to show that if the condition holds in a later case, it also must hold for the very next case after that.

In mathematical notation, proof by induction looks like this:

To prove that all positive integers n have some given property $P(n)$, prove these two conditions:

I. $P(1)$. (This means the number 1 obeys the property P.)

II. If $P(m)$, then $P(m + 1)$. (This means if some number m obeys the property P, then the next number $m + 1$ also obeys the property.)

Can you see how these two steps are similar to the steps in the examples of the domino chain and the ladder?

Now let's use mathematical induction to prove a conjecture about positive integers that you discovered in the first chapter of your geometry book. Look back at Exercise 22 from Exercise Set 1.5 of your *Discovering Geometry* text. In this problem, you find a pattern for adding sequences of positive integers. From this problem you can conclude that

$$1 + 2 + 3 + \ldots + n = \frac{n(n + 1)}{2}.$$

Although you probably already believe that this formula works for any positive integer, you haven't proved it yet. Let's use the two steps of mathematical induction to prove this conjecture.

I. First we prove that the conjecture holds for $n = 1$. A sequence of length 1 that begins with 1 only has the number 1 in it. This means we need to prove that

$$1 = \frac{1(1 + 1)}{2}.$$

Simplify the right side of the equation and see what you get. (You can do it in your head!)

II. Now we need to prove that if our conjecture works for some number m, then it also works for $m + 1$. Here is the setup for our proof. Can you see how we replaced m with its successor, $m + 1$, in the "prove" part?

Given: $1 + 2 + 3 + \ldots + m = \dfrac{m(m + 1)}{2}$

Prove: $1 + 2 + 3 + \ldots + m + (m + 1) = \dfrac{(m + 1)((m + 1) + 1)}{2}$

Since the first m terms of the sequence on the left in the "prove" are exactly the same terms as the sequence in the "given," we can substitute and get

$$\frac{m(m + 1)}{2} + (m + 1) = \frac{(m + 1)((m + 1) + 1)}{2}.$$

You'll need to use some algebra to prove that these two statements are the same. Once you do this, you have finished both parts of the proof by induction and the proof is complete.

1. Brush up on your algebra skills! Complete the sample proof above by showing that both sides of the last equation really mean the same thing.

Now you can write your own proofs using mathematical induction. For each of the remaining problems, copy and complete each statement, then prove the statement using mathematical induction. Set up both steps of each proof carefully.

2. "The sum of the first n odd numbers is equal to _____." (See Exercise 20, Exercise Set 1.5.)

3. "The sum of the first n even numbers is _____." (See Exercise 21, Exercise Set 1.5.)

4. "Suppose there are n people at a party. Also suppose every person shakes hands with every other person. There are a total of _____ handshakes." (See Investigation 1.6.)

Introduction to the Geometer's Sketchpad Demonstrations

Two disks accompany this book: One disk is for computers running Microsoft® Windows® (version 3.1 or later) and the other is for Macintosh® computers. Each disk contains a free demonstration version of The Geometer's Sketchpad, groundbreaking software for doing geometry dynamically, as well as seventeen Sketchpad sketches that demonstrate concepts from *Discovering Geometry*. The blackline masters that follow this introduction are designed to be used with the demonstration sketches.

The Geometer's Sketchpad Demonstration Version

The demonstration version of The Geometer's Sketchpad that comes on each disk is similar to the full-featured program except that you cannot save, print, or export your work. If you wish to use the software to do more than the demonstrations, you'll need to purchase the full-featured program. The Geometer's Sketchpad full-featured program comes with complete documentation, Teaching Notes with sample Activity Masters, an introductory video tape, and over 100 sketches and scripts. To purchase or preview the full-featured program, call Key Curriculum Press at 1-800-995-MATH. Federal copyright law prohibits unauthorized classroom use of the demonstration version.

You can run the demonstration version of Sketchpad and the demonstration sketches directly from the floppy disk or from your computer's hard disk. The action in the sketches will be faster and smoother if you copy the software and sketches onto a hard disk. Refer to your Windows or Macintosh manual for instructions on how to copy files to your hard disk and how to run software.

The Geometer's Sketchpad Demonstrations

No prior experience with The Geometer's Sketchpad is necessary to use the demonstrations. They're all designed to be investigated by simply dragging parts of the figure with the mouse and by double-clicking action buttons. The demonstrations are optimized for viewing on a color monitor. For simplicity's sake, Sketchpad's toolbox is hidden from view. None of the menu commands are required except the Open and Close commands in the File menu. Because the demonstrations are so easy to use, no documentation is provided for them.

Where possible, a large type font is used so that you can show the demonstrations with a computer connected to an overhead display device or to a large-screen monitor. Not all overhead projectors are bright enough (and not all classrooms can be made dark enough) for overhead demonstrations to be seen clearly. But if you have a working display, one way to use the sketches is to demonstrate them to your whole class yourself.

If you have a few (or even just one) computers in your class with no large-screen display, you can let small groups of students take turns working with the demonstrations while other students are working on the investigations in the text.

You can take students to a computer lab to work with the demonstrations. Be aware, though, that because the demonstrations don't require students to do any constructions of their own, few, if any, of the single demonstrations are likely to occupy students for a class period.

Familiarize yourself with each demonstration sketch and the accompanying activity master to form your own ideas about the best way to use them.

The Geometer's Sketchpad Demonstration Activity Masters

The activity masters in this book guide students toward things to look for while they're manipulating a sketch. The activities also ask guiding questions to ensure that students understand what the demonstration is about. Each activity is correlated to a lesson or lessons from *Discovering Geometry*.

The sketches themselves, however, are in large part self-explanatory. And to the extent to which the sketches are not self-explanatory, your students may enjoy the challenge of trying to figure out themselves what's going on. So you could simply set students loose with a sketch and ask them to explain what they think it demonstrates.

Discovering Geometry with The Geometer's Sketchpad

The demonstration sketches can give you some idea of Sketchpad's power as a Dynamic Geometry environment. But to exploit the program's full potential as a learning tool, students should use it to construct figures of their own and to carry out investigations starting from a blank sketch. To do so, students should have access to the full-featured program.

A separate book of activities titled *Discovering Geometry with The Geometer's Sketchpad* is also available from Key Curriculum Press. In most of the book's activities, students start with a blank sketch and perform a complete investigation from scratch. The activities are correlated with *Discovering Geometry* lessons. *Discovering Geometry with The Geometer's Sketchpad* assumes students have access to The Geometer's Sketchpad full-featured program. The disks that accompany the book do not include any version of the program itself.

Classifying Parallelograms

In this demonstration you'll manipulate four specially constructed quadrilaterals: a parallelogram, a rhombus, a rectangle, and a square. You'll see how they behave and how they are related to one another.

Investigate

Step 1   Open the sketch **Parallelograms** (Mac) or **Pgrams.gsp** (Windows).

Step 2   Use the Selection Arrow tool to drag different vertices of each shape. Play for a minute to get a feel for how these points control the shapes.

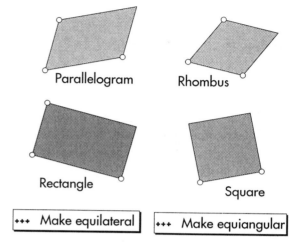

Questions

1.   Which of the four shapes would you say is the most flexible? Explain.

2.   Which of the four shapes would you say is the least flexible? Explain.

3.   Write a sentence or two about the flexibility of the other two shapes. Is one more flexible than the other? Explain.

4.   All four shapes are parallelograms, but the rectangle, rhombus, and square have additional properties. What property do all four parallelograms have in common?

Investigate

Step 3   Get ready to watch the four shapes, then double-click the Make equilateral button. You should see one or more of the shapes change. If you don't, try dragging different points to "mess up" each shape, then double-click the Make equilateral button again. Once each shape is equilateral, don't change it until you've answered the following questions.

Questions

5.   Which shapes changed when you double-clicked Make equilateral?

6.   Which shapes didn't change when you double-clicked Make equilateral? Explain.

7.   What shape does the parallelogram look like when it's equilateral?

8.   What shape does the rectangle look like when it's equilateral?

Investigate

Step 4   Drag different points to mess up each shape.

Step 5   Get ready to watch the four shapes, then double-click the Make equiangular button. Once each shape is equiangular, don't change it until you've answered the following questions.

Questions

9. Which shapes changed when you double-clicked Make equiangular?

10. Which shapes didn't change when you double-clicked Make equiangular? Explain.

11. What shape does the parallelogram look like when it's equiangular?

12. What shape does the rhombus look like when it's equiangular?

Investigate

Step 6   Drag different points to mess up each shape.

Step 7   Double-click both the Make equiangular button and the Make equilateral button, in either order.

Questions

13. What shape do all the parallelograms look like when they are equiangular and equilateral?
    Drag points and double-click the buttons as needed to answer the following questions.

14. Define *parallelogram*.

15. Define *rhombus*.

16. Define *rectangle*.

17. Define *square*.

18. Is a rectangle always, sometimes, or never a rhombus? Explain.

19. Is a square always, sometimes, or never a rectangle? Explain.

20. Is a parallelogram always, sometimes, or never a square? Explain.

21. At right is a concept map showing the relationships among some members of the parallelogram. This type of concept map is know as a **Venn diagram**. Fill in the missing names.

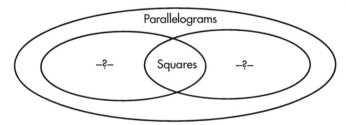

Points of Concurrency

In this demonstration you'll discover properties of several remarkable points associated with a triangle.

Investigate: Medians

Step 1   Open the sketch **Triangle Points** (Mac) or **Tripoint.gsp** (Windows).

Step 2   Double-click the Medians show button. You'll see the medians intersect in a single point. This point is called the **centroid**.

Step 3   Drag a vertex of the triangle and observe the medians.

Questions

1.   Do the medians always intersect in a single point, no matter what shape the triangle is?

2.   Watch the measurements as you drag. Into what ratio does the centroid divide each median?

Investigate: Altitudes

Step 4   Double-click the Medians hide button.

Step 5   Double-click the Altitudes show button. You'll see three lines that pass through the altitudes of the triangle. These lines intersect in a single point called the **orthocenter**.

Step 6   Drag a vertex of the triangle and observe the altitudes.

Questions

3.   Do the altitudes always intersect in a single point, no matter what shape the triangle is?

4.   Describe triangles in which the orthocenter falls inside, outside, or on the triangle. On what point does the orthocenter fall when it falls on the triangle?

Investigate: Angle Bisectors

Step 7   Double-click the Altitudes hide button.

Step 8   Double-click the Angle bisectors show button. You'll see the three angle bisectors intersecting in a single point. This point is called the **incenter**. The incenter is the center of the inscribed circle.

Step 9   Drag a vertex of the triangle and observe the angle bisectors and the inscribed circle.

Questions

5.   Do the angle bisectors always intersect in a single point, no matter what shape the triangle is?

6.   Explain why the incenter is the center of the inscribed circle. Hint: Any point on an angle bisector is —?— from the sides of the angle.

Medians

| ▲ Show | △ Hide |

Altitudes

| ••• Show | ••• Hide |

Angle bisectors

| ▲ Show | △ Hide |

Investigate: Perpendicular Bisectors

Step 10   Double-click the Angle bisectors hide button.

Step 11   Double-click the Perpendicular bisectors show button. You'll see the perpendicular bisectors of the three sides of the triangle intersecting in a single point. This point is called the **circumcenter**. The circumcenter is the center of the circumscribed circle.

Step 12   Drag a vertex of the triangle and observe the perpendicular bisectors and the circumscribed circle.

Questions

7.   Do the perpendicular bisectors always intersect in a single point, no matter what shape the triangle is?

8.   Describe triangles in which the circumcenter falls inside, outside, or on the triangle. On what point does the circumcenter fall when it falls on the triangle?

9.   Explain why the circumcenter is the center of the circumscribed circle. Hint: Any point on a perpendicular bisector of a segment is equidistant from —?—.

Investigate: The Euler Segment

Step 13   Double-click the Perpendicular bisectors hide button.

Step 14   Double-click the Euler segment show button. You'll see the four points of concurrency and a segment connecting three of them. Drag a vertex and observe the Euler segment.

Questions

10.   Which of the four points of concurrency is not usually on the Euler segment?

11.   Are the endpoints of the Euler segment always the same two points? If so, what points are they?

12.   What point is on the Euler segment but is not an endpoint? How does this point divide the Euler segment?

13.   In what kind of triangle are all four points of concurrency on the Euler segment?

14.   In what kind of triangle do all four points of concurrency coincide?

15.   Is it possible for two or three of the points of concurrency to coincide without the fourth joining in?

16.   In what kind of triangle do the endpoints of the Euler segment fall on the triangle? At what points do these endpoints fall?

Investigate: The Nine-Point Circle

Step 15   Double-click the Euler segment hide button.

Step 16   Double-click the 9-point circle show button. You'll see a circle with up to nine points on it. (Ignore the measurements for now.)

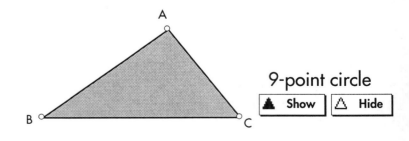

Questions

17. The nine-point circle passes through the three midpoints of the sides of the triangle. See whether you can determine what the other six points are and describe them. Hint: Double-click the Altitudes show button and drag the triangle.

18. As you drag the triangle, you may observe that points on the nine-point circle sometimes coincide. Make two of the nine points coincide so that only eight points are visible. What kind of triangle is this? Which two points coincide?

19. Describe all the triangles you can find in which fewer than eight of the points on the nine-point circle are visible. In each case, describe how many points are visible and which points coincide.

20. If the altitudes are showing, hide them, then show the angle bisectors. Drag the triangle. How are the inscribed circle and the nine-point circle related?

21. Hide the angle bisectors and show the perpendicular bisectors. Now you can pay attention to the measurements. How are the circumscribed circle and the nine-point circle related?

22. Hide the perpendicular bisectors and show the Euler segment along with the nine-point circle. What do you notice about the center of the nine-point circle and the Euler segment?

Geometer's Sketchpad Demonstration: Lesson 4.5

Equations of Lines

In this demonstration you'll look for relationships between the equation of a line and its slope and *y*-intercept.

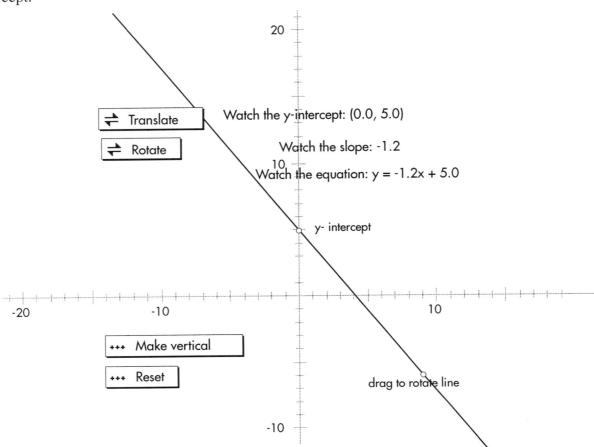

Investigate

Step 1   Open the sketch **Slope-Intercept Form** (Mac) or **Slopeint.gsp** (Windows).

Step 2   Double-click the Translate and Rotate action button and observe their effects on the line and on the measurements and equation.

Step 3   Drag the point *y-intercept* and the point *drag to rotate line* and observe what changes in the sketch. Experiment with these buttons and points as you answer the following questions. Do not double-click the Make vertical or Reset button until you've answered the questions.

Questions

1.   Dragging the point *y-intercept* has the same effect as what action button?

2.   What measurement changes when you double-click the Translate button?

3.   What part of the equation changes when you double-click the Translate button?

4.   Dragging the point *drag to rotate line* has the same effect as what action button?

5.   What measurement changes when you double-click the Rotate button?

6. What part of the equation changes when you double-click the Rotate button?
7. If the graph of a line has a slope of m and a y-intercept of $(0, b)$, what is the equation of the line? (This is called the **slope-intercept form of the equation of a line**.)
8. Make the line horizontal. What is its slope?
9. In slope-intercept form, what's the equation of a horizontal line?

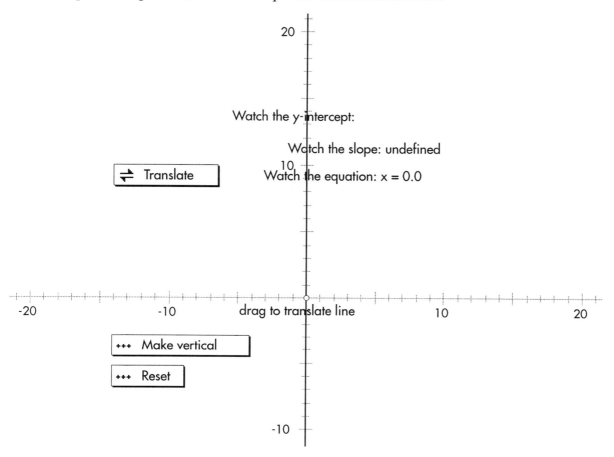

Investigate

Step 4   Double-click the Make vertical button and observe its effects. The line will become vertical and will remain vertical until you double-click the Reset button. Do not double-click Reset until you've answered the following questions.

Step 5   Double-click the Translate button or drag the point *drag to translate line*.

Questions

10. What's the equation of the line when it coincides with the y-axis?
11. What's the slope of a vertical line?
12. What measurement disappears when the line becomes vertical? Why?
13. What's the equation of a vertical line that intercepts the x-axis at a point $(0, c)$?
14. Explain why the variable y doesn't appear in the equation of a vertical line.

Triangle Sum Conjecture

This sketch demonstrates a property of the angles of any triangle. The sketch also demonstrates why this property holds.

Investigate

Step 1   Open the sketch **Triangle Sum** (Mac) or **Trisum.gsp** (Windows).

Step 2   Drag each vertex of the triangle and observe how the angle measures change.

Step 3   Double-click the Show sum button.

Step 4   Drag each vertex again and observe the effect on the sum.

Step 5   Double-click the Show why button, then double-click each of the two buttons that appear, observing the effects of each button.

Step 6   Double-click the Reset button, change the triangle, and repeat the Show why button demonstration.

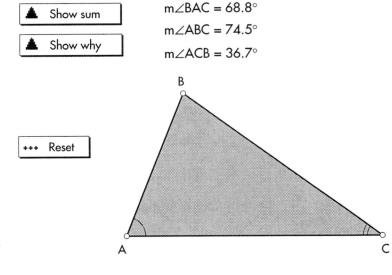

m∠BAC = 68.8°

m∠ABC = 74.5°

m∠ACB = 36.7°

Questions

1.   What's the sum of the angle measures in any triangle?

2.   Write a paragraph or two explaining how the Show why button demonstration demonstrates why the sum of the angle measures in a triangle is what it is. Include diagrams in your explanation.

Exterior Angles of a Polygon

If you extend each side of a polygon in the same orientation (clockwise or counterclockwise), you create a set of exterior angles. In this demonstration you'll investigate the sum of the measures of one set of exterior angles in a polygon.

Investigate

Step 1 Open the sketch **Exterior Angles** (Mac) or **Extang.gsp** (Windows).

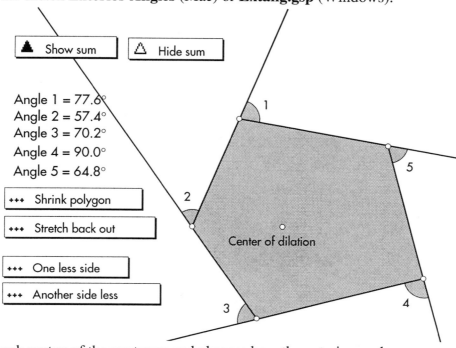

Step 2 Drag each vertex of the pentagon and observe how the exterior angle measures change.

Step 3 Double-click the Show sum button.

Step 4 Drag each vertex again and observe the effect on the sum.

Step 5 Make sure the polygon is convex, then double-click the Shrink polygon button. Observe the effects of the button on the polygon and the angle measures.

Step 6 To repeat the experiment for another pentagon, double-click the Stretch back out button, drag one or more vertices to change the polygon, then shrink it again.

Step 7 To try the experiment for a quadrilateral, stretch the polygon back out, double-click the One less side button, then shrink the polygon.

Step 8 To try the experiment for a triangle, stretch the quadrilateral back out, double-click the Another side less button, then shrink the polygon.

Questions

1. What's the sum of the measures of one set of exterior angles in any pentagon, quadrilateral, or triangle?

2. Do you think your answer to Question 1 can be generalized for any polygon? If so, explain why you think the sum of the measures of one set of exterior angles is what it is.

3. Explain what happens to exterior angles and their sum when the polygon is nonconvex.

Geometer's Sketchpad Demonstration: Lesson 7.5

The Circumference/Diameter Ratio

If you make a circle bigger, you increase both the distance across it (its diameter) and the distance around it (its circumference). The ratio of the circumference to diameter is the same for any circle. In this demonstration you'll investigate this ratio.

Investigate

Step 1   Open the sketch **Circumference/Diameter** (Mac) or **Circdiam.gsp** (Windows).

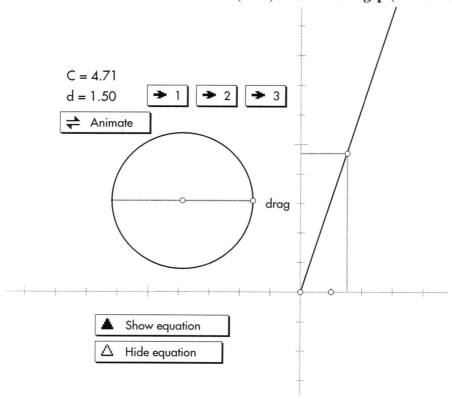

Step 2   Change the diameter of the circle in any of three ways: (1) by dragging the point drag; (2) by double-clicking the 1, 2, or 3 buttons; or (3) by double-clicking the Animate button.

Step 3   Observe how changing the size of the circle affects the point on the graph. Experiment with the sketch to answer the following questions, but don't double-click the Show equation button until you've tried answering the questions.

Questions

1.   What does the value of the *x*-coordinate of the point on the graph represent?
2.   What does the value of the *y*-coordinate of the point on the graph represent?
3.   The ratio of the circumference of the circle to its diameter is a constant represented by the Greek letter π (pi). What is the value of π to the nearest thousandth?
4.   What is the value of the slope of the line? What does the slope represent?
5.   What is the equation of the line in terms of *x* and *y*? Double-click the Show equation button to confirm your answer.
6.   Rewrite the equation for the line in terms of *C*, *d*, and π.

Geometer's Sketchpad Demonstration: Lesson 8.2

Properties of Isometries

When one isometry is applied to a figure and then another isometry is applied to the figure's image, the resulting transformation is called the **composition of isometries**. In this demonstration you'll discover what transformations result from the composition of two reflections. First you'll investigate reflections across parallel lines. Then you'll investigate reflections across lines that intersect.

Investigate: Reflections Across Parallel Lines

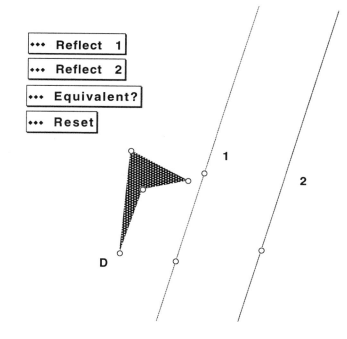

Step 1　Open the sketch **Reflections/Parallel** (Mac) or **Ref_para.gsp** (Windows).

Step 2　Double-click the Reflect 1 button. You'll see an image of the polygon move over to the other side of line 1 and come to rest as the mirror image of the polygon. While it's moving, imagine that it's coming out of the plane of your computer screen.

Step 3　Drag the vertices of the original polygon and drag the line. Watch the effects on the image.

Step 4　Double-click the Reflect 2 button. You'll see an image of the first mirror image move over to the other side of line 2 and come to rest as the mirror image of the first image.

Step 5　Drag the vertices of the original polygon and of both images. Drag both lines. Observe how the original image and the first and second mirror images are related to each other.

Step 6　*Before* you double-click the Equivalent? button, make a guess about what single transformation would move the original polygon to the second mirror image.

Step 7　Double-click the Equivalent? button to check your guess.

Step 8　Double-click the Reset button, move objects in the sketch around, and repeat the experiment to help you answer the following questions.

Questions

1.　What single transformation is equivalent to the composition of two reflections across parallel lines?

2.　How is the direction and the distance of this transformation related to the lines?

Investigate: Reflections Across Intersecting Lines

Step 9   Open the sketch
Reflections/Intersecting (Mac) or
Ref_inter.gsp (Windows).

Step 10   Experiment with this sketch as you did in
the parallel lines sketch to answer the
following questions.

Questions

3. What single transformation is equivalent to
the composition of two reflections across
intersecting lines?

4. How is this transformation related to the angle
between the lines?

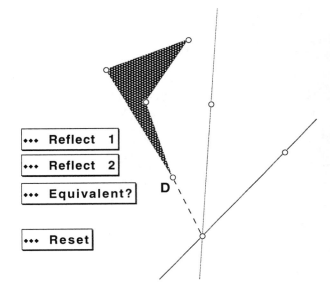

Tessellations

In Lessons 8.6–8.8, you created tessellations using translations, rotations, and glide reflections. Your challenge in this demonstration is to analyze two Sketchpad tessellations to determine what the basic grid beneath each tessellation is and to determine what transformations were used to create the tile.

Investigate

Step 1   Open the sketch **Tessellation 1** (Mac) or **Tess_1** (Windows).

Step 2   *Before* you double-click the Morph to grid button, drag the vertices of the dark-shaded polygon. Observe how each vertex affects the other vertices of the tile.

Step 3   Make a guess about what polygon (parallelogram, square, equilateral triangle, regular hexagon, kite, etc.) forms the basic grid of this tessellation.

Step 4   Double-click the Morph to grid button to check your guess.

Step 5   Drag each point on each edge of the tile. As you drag each point, identify which point is the image of that point under some transformation. Try to determine what the transformation is.

••• Morph to grid

Questions

1.   What shape forms the basic grid of the tessellation?

2.   What transformations were used in the tessellation?

Investigate

Step 6   Open the sketch **Tessellation 2** (Mac) or **Tess_2** (Windows).

Step 7   *Before* you double-click the Morph to grid button, drag the vertices of the dark-shaded polygon. Observe how each vertex affects the other vertices of the tile.

Step 8   Make a guess about what polygon (parallelogram, square, equilateral triangle, regular hexagon, kite, etc.) forms the basic grid of this tessellation.

Step 9   Double-click the Morph to grid button to check your guess.

Step 10   Drag each point on each edge of the tile. As you drag each point, identify which point is the image of that point under some transformation. Try to determine what the transformation is.

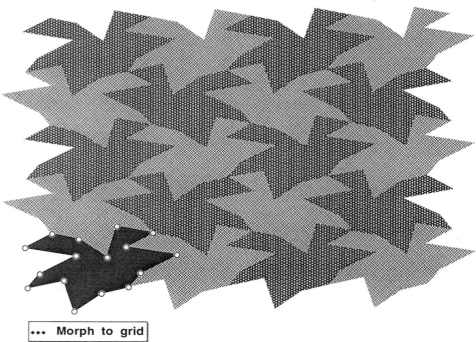

Morph to grid

Questions

3.   What shape forms the basic grid of the tessellation?

4.   What transformations were used in the tessellation?

Areas of Triangles and Trapezoids

This demonstration shows how triangles and trapezoids are related to a shape whose area you already know how to find. From this relationship you'll derive formulas for the areas of triangles and trapezoids.

Investigate: Triangle Area

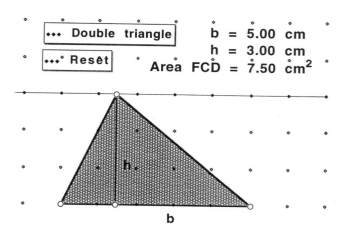

Step 1   Open the sketch **Triangle Area** (Mac) or **Tri_area.gsp** (Windows).

Step 2   *Before* you double-click any action buttons, drag parts of the triangle to see how they behave and how they affect the measurements in the sketch. You can change the base of the triangle by dragging either endpoint of the base. You can move the top vertex of the triangle along a line parallel to the base without changing the triangle's height. To change the triangle's height, drag the line through the top vertex up and down.

Step 3   Double-click the Double triangle button.

Step 4   Drag different parts of the sketch and observe how the doubled triangle compares to the original triangle.

Questions

1. Describe how you can change the shape of the triangle without changing its area. Why doesn't the area change in that case?

2. Describe two ways in which you can change the area of the triangle.

3. What kind of shape is formed when you double the triangle? What is the area of this shape in terms of b and h?

4. What is the area of the triangle in terms of b and h?

Investigate: Trapezoid Area

Step 5   Open the sketch **Trapezoid Area** (Mac) or **Traparea.gsp** (Windows).

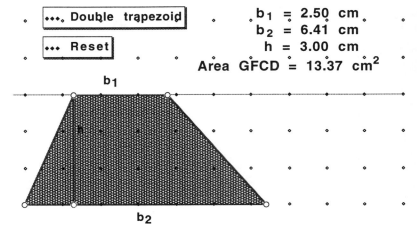

Step 6   *Before* you double-click any action buttons, drag parts of the trapezoid to see how they behave and how they affect the measurements in the sketch. You can change either base of the trapezoid by dragging either endpoint of the base. You can drag segment b_1 along a line parallel to segment b_2 without changing the trapezoid's height. To change the trapezoid's height, drag the line through segment b_1 up and down.

Step 7   Double-click the Double trapezoid button.

Step 8   Drag different parts of the sketch and observe how the doubled trapezoid compares to the original trapezoid.

Questions

5. Describe how you can change the shape of the trapezoid without changing its area. Why doesn't the area change in that case?

6. Describe three ways in which you can change the area of the trapezoid.

7. What kind of shape is formed when you double the trapezoid? What is the area of this shape in terms of b_1, b_2, and h?

8. What is the area of the trapezoid in terms of b_1, b_2, and h?

The Theorem of Pythagoras

The Pythagorean Theorem describes a special relationship among the legs and the hypotenuse of any right triangle. This demonstration shows how squares constructed on the legs of a right triangle can be dissected into pieces that fit into the square on the hypotenuse.

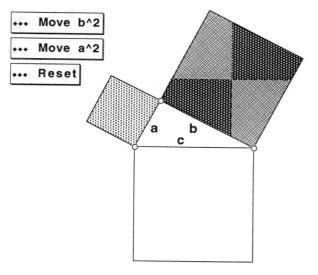

Investigate

Step 1   Open the sketch **Pythagorean Theorem** (Mac) or **Pytheorm.gsp** (Windows).

Step 2   Drag each vertex of the triangle and observe how the shapes change.

Step 3   Double-click the Move b^2 and Move a^2 action buttons.

Step 4   Drag each vertex of the triangle again.

Step 5   Double-click the Reset button and repeat the experiment.

Questions

1.   If the short leg of the triangle has length *a*, what's the area of the square constructed on that leg?

2.   If the long leg of the triangle has length *b*, what's the area of the square constructed on that leg?

3.   If the hypotenuse of the triangle has length *c*, what's the area of the square constructed on it in terms of *c*?

4.   What did clicking the Move a^2 and Move b^2 buttons demonstrate?

5.   What's the area of the square constructed on the hypotenuse in terms of *a* and *b*?

6.   Write an equation that relates *a*, *b*, and *c*.

Geometer's Sketchpad Demonstration: Lesson 12.6

Proportions with Area

Elias is building his dream house. He has decided to double the length and the width of the master bathroom from its dimensions in the original plans. Does that mean he should buy twice as much floor tile? In this demonstration you'll investigate how the ratio of the areas of similar figures compares to the ratio of corresponding lengths.

Investigate

Step 1   Open the sketch **Area Proportions** (Mac) or **Areaprop.gsp** (Windows).

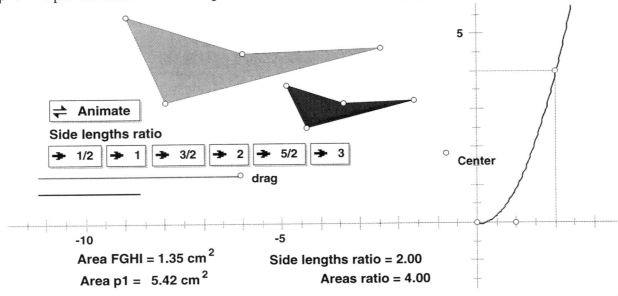

Area FGHI = 1.35 cm^2

Area p1 = 5.42 cm^2

Side lengths ratio = 2.00

Areas ratio = 4.00

Step 2   The lighter polygon is the image of the darker polygon dilated by a scale factor defined by the two horizontal segments. Drag different vertices of the two polygons to confirm that the polygons are always similar.

Step 3   Change the scale factor by double-clicking the Animate button, by double-clicking any of the buttons with numbers on them, or by dragging the point *drag*. Watch the effect different scale factors have on the areas ratio and on the graph.

Questions

1.   How can you tell from their appearance that the two polygons are similar?

2.   The side lengths ratio displayed in the sketch is the ratio of (choose a or b):

    a. the dark polygon's side lengths to the light polygon's side lengths

    b. the light polygon's side lengths to the dark polygon's side lengths

3.   Copy and complete the table below. Write the area ratios as fractions.

Side lengths ratio	1/2	1	3/2	2	5/2	3
Area ratio	–?–	–?–	–?–	–?–	–?–	–?–

4.   Explain what the graph represents.

5.   If you double all the dimensions of a figure, does the resulting similar figure have twice the area?

Non-Euclidean Geometries

Most of the geometry you've studied is based on the postulates of Euclid, a Greek mathematician who lived around 300 B.C. Euclid's fifth postulate, known as the **Parallel Postulate**, states that through a point not on a given line, you can construct exactly one line parallel to the given line. Postulates are supposed to be self-evident enough not to require proof, but for centuries the Parallel Postulate didn't seemed self-evident to mathematicians. Many mathematicians tried and failed to prove the postulate. Then, in the nineteenth century, several mathematicians experimented with geometric systems in which the Parallel Postulate was assumed *not* to be true. One such geometry can be modeled on what's called the Poincaré disk. In this demonstration you'll explore lines and triangles on the Poincaré disk.

Investigate

Step 1   Open the sketch **Poincaré Lines** (Mac) or **Poincar1.gsp** (Windows). You'll see the Poincaré disk with four "lines" drawn on it.

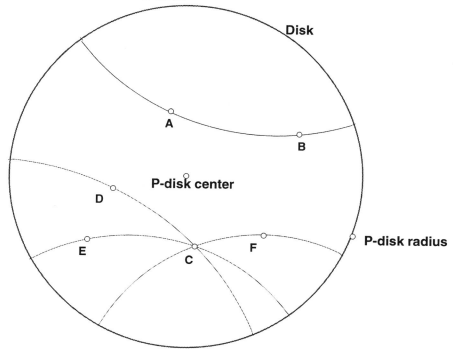

Step 2   Drag the points to see how they control the lines.

Questions

1.   Describe in as much detail as you can what a line is in the Poincaré disk.

2.   Do you think that through two points on the Poincaré disk there is exactly one line? Explain.

3.   Parallel lines are lines that don't intersect. Drag points *C, D, E,* and *F* so that none of the three lines through point *C* intersect line *AB*. Do you think other lines could be constructed through point *C* parallel to line *AB*? If so, how many others?

4.   The Poincaré disk is a model of **hyperbolic geometry**. Rewrite the Parallel Postulate as it applies in hyperbolic geometry.

Investigate

Next you'll investigate one of the consequences of the altered Parallel Postulate in hyperbolic geometry.

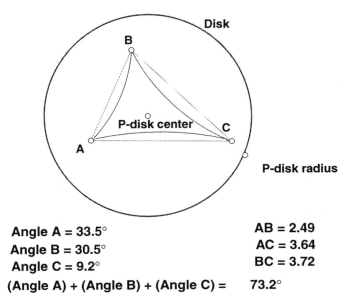

Step 3 Open the sketch **Poincaré Triangle** (Mac) or **Poincar2.gsp** (Windows). You'll see the Poincaré disk with a Poincaré triangle drawn on it. Drawn with dashed segments around the Poincaré triangle is a Euclidean triangle.

Step 4 Drag the vertices of the triangle and observe the triangle and the measurements.

Angle A = 33.5°
Angle B = 30.5°
Angle C = 9.2°
(Angle A) + (Angle B) + (Angle C) = 73.2°

AB = 2.49
AC = 3.64
BC = 3.72

Questions

5. In a Euclidean triangle, the sum of the angle measures is a constant 180°. The angles measured in this sketch are the angles in the Poincaré triangle. Describe everything you observe about the sum of the angle measures in a Poincaré triangle.

6. Describe triangles in which the sum of the angle measures is least.

7. Describe triangles in which the sum of the angle measures is greatest.

8. Drag a vertex of the triangle to make two of the length measurements approximately equal. Distances appear distorted to our Euclidean eyes in the Poincaré disk, so the triangle won't necessarily appear to be isosceles. Do the base angles have equal measure?

Special Midpoint Quadrilaterals

In Lesson 16.7, you proved that the quadrilateral formed by connecting the midpoints of the sides of any quadrilateral is a parallelogram. You also proved that some special quadrilaterals have special parallelograms for their midpoint quadrilaterals. For example, the midpoint quadrilateral of a rectangle is a rhombus. But are rectangles the only quadrilaterals whose midpoint quadrilaterals are rhombuses? In this demonstration you'll investigate quadrilaterals whose midpoint quadrilaterals are special parallelograms.

Investigate

Step 1   Open the sketch **Special Midpoint Quads** (Mac) or **Mdptquad.gsp** (Windows). You'll see three quadrilaterals that have special parallelograms for midpoint quadrilaterals. *Don't* double-click the Show clues button until you've tried to answer Questions 1–3.

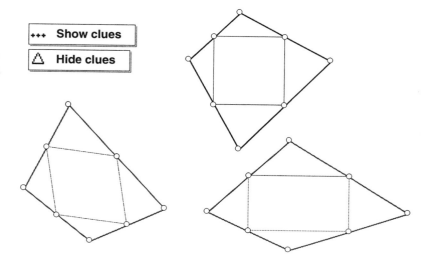

Step 2   Drag the vertices and the midpoints to see how they control the quadrilaterals.

Questions

1.   The three quadrilaterals don't appear to be special, but when you try to drag them you should see that they do behave in unexpected ways. Still, you may not immediately see what defines them. Continue dragging points to try to see what's special about the quadrilateral whose midpoint quadrilateral is a rhombus. What characteristics define this quadrilateral? If you're stuck, try answering Questions 2 and 3 before you show the clues.

2.   What characteristics define the quadrilateral whose midpoint quadrilateral is a rectangle?

3.   What characteristics define the quadrilateral whose midpoint quadrilateral is a square? If you get stuck trying to answer these questions, double-click the Show clues button. Then drag each quadrilateral and observe the clues.

4.   Prove that any quadrilateral that has the characteristics of the quadrilateral in Question 1 will have a rhombus for its midpoint quadrilateral.

5.   Prove that any quadrilateral that has the characteristics of the quadrilateral in Question 2 will have a rectangle for its midpoint quadrilateral.

6.   Prove that any quadrilateral that has the characteristics of the quadrilateral in Question 3 will have a square for its midpoint quadrilateral.

Teachers Notes and Answers for the Geometer's Sketchpad Demonstrations

Classifying Parallelograms

Use this demonstration with Lesson 2.7: Special Quadrilaterals. In the activity, students define *parallelogram, rhombus, rectangle,* and *square,* but they do not define *trapezoid* and *kite.* Question 21 in the demonstration is the same as Exercise 30 in Exercise Set 2.7. You may need to review the terms *equilateral* and *equiangular.*

Answers

1. Answers may vary. The most common answer should be the parallelogram. It's possible to change both its angles and its side lengths by dragging any of the three points.

2. Answers may vary. The most common answer should be the square. Dragging either of the two points changes the side lengths, but the four lengths remain equal to each other. It's not possible to change the angles.

3. Answers may vary. Some students may find the rectangle more flexible because it's possible to make the side lengths unequal. But it's not possible to change the angles. Some students may find the rhombus more flexible because it's possible to change the angles. But it's not possible to make the side lengths unequal.

4. Opposite sides are parallel.

5. The parallelogram and rectangle should change when students click Make equilateral. (If students get a message that says "Nothing will move now . . . ," tell them to ignore it and click OK.)

6. The rhombus and the square don't change because they're already equilateral.

7. A rhombus

8. A square

9. The parallelogram and the rhombus

10. The rectangle and the square don't change because they're already equiangular.

11. A rectangle

12. A square

13. A square

14. A parallelogram is a quadrilateral with opposite sides parallel.

15. A rhombus is an equilateral quadrilateral.

16. A rectangle is an equiangular quadrilateral.

17. A square is an equilateral and equiangular quadrilateral (or an equilateral rectangle, or an equiangular rhombus).

18. A rectangle is sometimes a rhombus. It is a rhombus when it is equilateral, in which case it is also a square.

19. A square is always a rectangle because it is an equiangular quadrilateral.

20. A parallelogram is sometimes a square. It is a square when it is equilateral and equiangular.

Discovering Geometry Teacher's Resource Book

21.

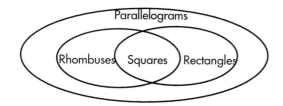

Points of Concurrency

This demonstration covers the material in Lessons 3.7 and 3.8 and then some. There are a ton of questions to answer, but students can go as far as they choose (or as far as you choose to give them time to go).

Answers

1. Yes

2. 2:1

3. Yes

4. The orthocenter falls inside an acute triangle, outside an obtuse triangle, and at the right angle vertex of a right triangle.

5. Yes

6. Any point on an angle bisector is equidistant from the sides of the angle. So the point at the intersection of the three angle bisectors is equidistant from all three sides of the triangle. Hence, a circle that has that distance for its radius will be inscribed in the triangle.

7. Yes

8. The circumcenter falls inside an acute triangle, outside an obtuse triangle, and at the midpoint of the hypotenuse of a right triangle.

9. Any point on the perpendicular bisector of a segment is equidistant from the endpoints of the segment. The circumcenter is on all three of the perpendicular bisectors of the sides of the triangle, so it is equidistant from all three vertices of the triangle. Hence, a circle centered at the circumcenter that passes through one vertex of the triangle will pass through all three, circumscribing the triangle.

10. The incenter

11. Yes, the circumcenter and the orthocenter

12. The centroid is on the Euler segment and divides it into two parts whose lengths are in a 2:1 ratio.

13. Isosceles

14. Equilateral

15. No. If any two points of concurrency coincide, all four do.

16. In a right triangle, the orthocenter falls at the right angle vertex and the circumcenter falls at the midpoint of the hypotenuse.

17. Besides the three midpoints, the nine-point circle passes through the three points at which the altitudes intersect the sides of the triangle. The other three points are the midpoints between each vertex and the orthocenter.

18. In an isosceles triangle, the point at which the altitude intersects the base coincides with the midpoint of the base.

19. In an equilateral triangle, the foot of each altitude coincides with a midpoint, so only six of the nine points are visible. In a right triangle, the feet of two altitudes and the midpoint between the right angle vertex and the orthocenter all coincide at the right angle vertex, so only five of the nine points are visible. In an isosceles right triangle, the foot of the third altitude coincides with the midpoint of a side, so only four of the nine points are visible.

20. The inscribed circle is internally tangent to the nine-point circle.

21. The circumscribed circle has radius twice that of the nine-point circle.

22. The center of the nine-point circle is the midpoint of the Euler segment.

Equations of Lines

This demonstration covers some of the material in Lesson 4.5, though students don't get practice writing equations of lines given point coordinates. They do discover where the slope and the y-intercept appear in the slope-intercept form of the equation of a line. They also discover the equation form for horizontal and vertical lines.

Answers

1. The Translate button
2. The y-intercept changes, but the slope doesn't.
3. The constant term at the end of the equation
4. The Rotate button
5. The slope changes, but the y-intercept doesn't.
6. The coefficient of x
7. $y = mx + b$
8. Zero
9. $y = 0x + b$, or simply $y = b$
10. $x = 0$
11. Undefined
12. The y-intercept disappears because a vertical line doesn't intersect the y-axis (except in the case where it coincides with the y-axis).
13. $x = c$
14. For any point on a vertical line the x-coordinate is a constant, regardless of the y-coordinate.

Triangle Sum Conjecture

This demonstration is equivalent to Investigation 5.1.1, in which students tear off the angles of a triangle and arrange them along a straight line. In addition, this demonstration previews the proof of the Triangle Sum Conjecture. (Although students aren't asked for a formal proof, they are asked to explain why the conjecture is true.)

Answers

1. 180°
2. When a line parallel to a side of the triangle is constructed through the vertex of the opposite angle, it forms two additional angles, each of which is congruent to one of the other two angles in the triangle. (The parallel line forms two pairs of corresponding angles.) Because the three angles form a straight line, the sum of their measures is 180°.

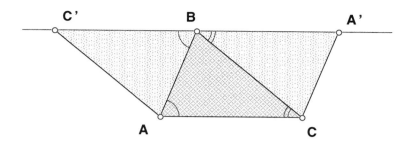

Exterior Angles of a Polygon

This is a convincing demonstration of why the sum of the measures of one set of exterior angles in any polygon is 360°. The issue of exterior angles in nonconvex polygons can get complicated, so consider offering extra credit for thoughtful responses to Question 3.

Answers

1. 360°

2. It doesn't matter how many sides the polygon has or what shape it is. When it is shrunk to a single point, one set of exterior angles surrounds that point. Thus, the sum of the angle measures is the same as one complete revolution around a point, or 360°.

3. Answers will vary. One possible answer: In a nonconvex polygon, one or more interior angles have measure greater than 180°. At each such angle, the "exterior" angle falls inside the triangle. To form a linear pair with the angle whose measure is greater than 180°, the exterior angle has to be subtracted from it. Because its orientation is different from the other exterior angles, it can be considered to have a negative measure, in which case the sum of the exterior angle measures is still 360°.

The Circumference/Diameter Ratio

In this demonstration the circumference/diameter ratio (π) is represented graphically.

Answers

1. The diameter of the circle

2. The circumference of the circle

3. 3.142

4. The slope of the line is 3.14. It represents the constant circumference/diameter ratio (π).

5. $y = 3.14x$

6. $C = \pi d$

Properties of Isometries

These demonstrations cover Investigations 8.2.2 and 8.2.3. You may need to explain that the motion of a reflection, unlike the motions of a translation or a rotation, brings the figure out of the plane. These demonstrations were made so that the polygon appears to come out of the plane while it's being reflected.

Answers

1. A translation

2. The direction is perpendicular to the two lines, and the distance is equal to twice the distance between the two lines.

3. A rotation

4. The angle of rotation is twice the measure of the angle between the lines.

Tessellations

Don't be discouraged (and don't let students get discouraged) if students can't figure out what transformations were applied in these tessellations. They'll still enjoy playing with the demonstrations, and if you decide at some point to reveal the answers to Questions 3 and 4, students will have an easier time seeing the transformations at work.

Answers

1. An equilateral triangle

2. The left and bottom sides of the dark-shaded tile are related by a 60° rotation. The right side has point symmetry. Other tiles in the tessellation are related by 60°, 120°, and 180° rotations.

3. A parallelogram

4. The top and bottom edges of the dark-shaded tile are related by a glide reflection. The left and right edges are related by a translation. Other tiles in the tessellation are related by translations and glide reflections.

Areas of Triangles and Trapezoids

These demonstrations cover Investigations 9.2.1 and 9.2.2. They do not cover kite area.

Answers

1. Dragging the top vertex changes the triangle's shape without change its area. This point is on a line parallel to the triangle's base, so dragging it doesn't change the height or base of the triangle.

2. By changing the height (dragging the parallel line up and down) or by changing the length of the base (dragging one of its endpoints)

3. A parallelogram, $A = bh$

4. $A = \frac{1}{2} bh$

5. Dragging the segment b_1 changes the shape of the trapezoid without changing its area. The segment is on a line parallel to the trapezoid's base, so dragging it doesn't change the height or either base of the trapezoid.

6. By changing the height (dragging the parallel line up and down) or by changing the length of either base (dragging an endpoint of either base)

7. A parallelogram with bases $b_1 + b_2$ and height h, $A = (b_1 + b_2)h$

8. $A = \frac{1}{2} (b_1 + b_2)h$

The Theorem of Pythagoras

This demonstration covers Investigation 10.1

Answers

1. a^2
2. b^2
3. c^2
4. The sum of the areas of the squares on the legs of the right triangle is equal to the area of the square on the hypotenuse.
5. $a^2 + b^2$
6. $c^2 = a^2 + b^2$

Proportions with Area

This demonstration shows graphically how the ratio of areas of similar figures is related to the ratio of side lengths, the concept covered by Investigation 12.6.1. Students should still do the investigation so that they can practice applying the concept.

Answers

1. They have the same shape. (Corresponding angles are congruent, and corresponding sides are proportional.)
2. b
3.

Side lengths ratio	1/2	1	3/2	2	5/2	3
Area ratio	1/4	1	9/4	4	25/4	9

4. The x-axis of the graph represents the side lengths ratio, and the y-axis represents the areas ratio. The graph shows that the areas ratio is equal to the square of the side lengths ratio. (Its equation is $y = x^2$.)
5. No, doubling the dimensions of a figure results in a figure with four times the area.

Non-Euclidean Geometries

The introduction to this demonstration gives a very brief background on non-Euclidean geometry. For a little more depth, including a description of a model for elliptic geometry, see Project: Non-Euclidean Geometries in Chapter 15 of the student text.

Answers

1. Answers will vary. Students should at least note that Poincaré lines are arcs of circles that have endpoints on the disk. They may also notice that the arcs meet the disk at right angles.
2. Through two points there is exactly one Poincaré line. Students may have difficulty seeing this because, in general, many arcs can pass through two points. Only one arc, however, passes through two points and meets the Poincaré disk at right angles.
3. Infinitely many lines pass through point C that are parallel to line AB.
4. Through a point not on a given line there are infinitely many lines parallel to the given line.

5. Answers will vary. One possible answer: The sum of the angle measures in a Poincaré triangle varies and is greater than 0° and less than 180°.

6. Triangles whose vertices are closest to the edge of the disk have the least angle measure sum (closest to 0°).

7. Triangles whose vertices are closest to the center of the disk have the greatest angle measure sum (closest to 180°).

8. Yes

Special Midpoint Quadrilaterals

In this demonstration, students experiment with the most general quadrilaterals whose midpoints form special parallelograms. The questions are extensions to the proofs in Exercise Set 16.7.

Answers

1. The diagonals are congruent.

2. The diagonals are perpendicular.

3. The diagonals are perpendicular and congruent.

4. Answers will vary. One possible answer: Segment *EF* is a midsegment in △*ABC*, so *EF* = (1/2)*AC*. Segment *FG* is a midsegment of △*BCD*, so *FG* = (1/2)*BD*. Because *AC* = *BD*, *EF* = *FG*. By the same reasoning, *GH* = *HE* = *EF* = *FG*. Therefore, *EFGH* is a rhombus.

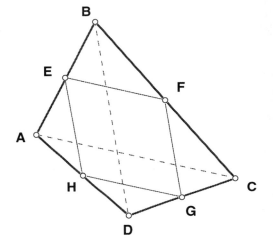

5. Answers will vary. One possible answer: Segment *QP* is a midsegment in △*KNL*, so *QP* is parallel to *KL*. Segment *PS* is a midsegment of △*NLM*, so *PS* is parallel to *NM*. Because *NM* is perpendicular to *KL*, *QP* is perpendicular to *PS*. By the same reasoning, *PS* is perpendicular to *SR* and *SR* is perpendicular to *RQ*. Therefore, *QPSR* is a rectangle.

6. Answers will vary. One possible answer: Using the same reasoning as in the answers to Questions 4 and 5, the midpoint quadrilateral is a rhombus and a rectangle. Therefore, it is a square.

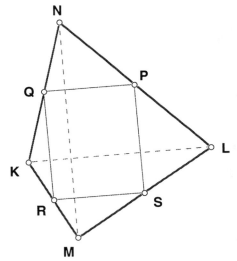

Introduction to the Annotated Bibliography and Lists of Geometry Resources

Sheldon G. Berman, Mathematics Department Head, Dobbins Vocational/Technical High School, Philadelphia, Pennsylvania

Engaging teachers—with the keen senses of early humans—are "hunter-gatherers," forever foraging for new and different materials with which to entice and challenge their students. (To visualize this, I must be reading too much Michael Serra and Gary Larson.) An attempt to share the results of years of foraging is represented by the annotated bibliography and lists in the following pages. All the books, posters, visuals, software, manipulatives, puzzles, toys, videos, and items from the bibliography and lists have been used to stimulate and support the study of high school geometry. The materials can easily be adapted for use with students on a more elementary or more advanced level.

Every entry in the bibliography and lists has qualities that make it notable as a resource for teaching geometry. The brief descriptions and the chart displaying ratings for each item indicate the special strengths and weaknesses of each entry. This information is intended to guide you in selecting appropriate materials for the type of students or emphasis particular to your classroom situation. The judgments made in compiling and evaluating the entries are mostly mine, and these judgments reflect both my experiences (working primarily with "regular" students in an inner-city setting and with teachers from a wide range of settings) and my fundamental belief that:

- Geometry is not an isolated content area. Mathematics, science, logic, critical thinking, visualizing, representing time-space relationships, skill in perceiving, and language skills are all intimately interwoven and inexorably united with the study of geometry.

- Geometric knowledge is accrued through both inductive and deductive processes. Our curiosity about phenomena and events in our immediate environment leads us through explorations to discoveries and understanding.

- Geometry is ever-present in human and natural design; an appreciation of this reality cannot be overemphasized! Geometry is included in mathematics curricula at all levels because it is so essential to describing our world. To reflect this significance, high school geometry must include much more than two-column proofs!

- Learning is most powerful when it is accompanied by some active, personal involvement. "Hands-on" activities in geometry (and in all subjects) are strongly recommended and are feasible in virtually every phase of learning.

Although many excellent publications are listed in the bibliography, the following three documents should be viewed as essential resources. Together they represent our best thinking about modern geometry and about what students should know and be able to do to become productive and effective citizens in a technological society.

- National Council of Teachers of Mathematics, Curriculum & Evaluation Standards for School Mathematics, Reston, VA: NCTM, 1989
  This far-reaching document is likely to influence the direction of change in mathematics education into the next decade, reflecting the dramatic changes heralding the age of information and the technological revolution.

- Coxford, A., Standards Addenda Series, Grades 9–12: Geometry from Multiple Perspectives, Reston, VA: NCTM, 1991

  The Addenda Series offers definitive exemplars of what implementing the Standards looks like in the classroom. Geometry from Multiple Perspectives contains dialogue centered around eighteen specific activities. Each activity is accompanied by thought provoking sidebar commentaries under Teaching Matters, Assessment Matters, and Try This suggestions. The thrust of the book is to engage geometry not only in terms of geometric properties, but also in terms of algebraic and matrix transformations, technological investigations, naturally occurring phenomena, and practical applications.

- American Association for the Advancement of Science (AAAS), Benchmarks for Science Literacy, New York: Oxford University Press, 1993

  A by-product of the AAAS Project 2061 work, the Benchmarks are every bit as significant as the NCTM Standards. Not only do the Benchmarks address content standards in mathematics, science, and technology, but they do it with specificity and at grade levels K–2, 3–5, 6–8, and 9–12. As the Standards do, the Benchmarks imply a pedagogy that emphasizes careful experimentation and the critical evaluation of data. A document that makes cross-references between the Standards and the Benchmarks is available through the AAAS Project 2061, (202) 842-5196.

Geometry Books and Visuals

The books and visual materials listed here are evaluated on a scale from 5+ (high) to 1 (low) for the following categories: visual impact, intellectual rigor, value as a teacher resource, and value as a resource for student activities. In addition, where appropriate, entries include a lesson or chapter number from the *Discovering Geometry* text, indicating when you could bring these treasures out of hiding and present them to your students. I suggest you share these materials with your students gradually, as the year unfolds, so that they have a better chance to appreciate the materials.

Visual impact: Visual impact signifies how well a book combines bold graphics, image "density," and outstanding photography to clearly illustrate the inherent mathematical or geometric beauty connoted by naturally occurring phenomena or the products of human design and engineering. The more a book consists of mostly written communication, the lower its rating.

Intellectual rigor: Rigor describes the correctness, completeness, and clarity of the explanations and theories presented in a book. The more completely the book details the mathematics involved, the higher its rating.

Teacher resource: If thoughts and images are the jewels of education, then books are the educator's treasure trove. Some books are perceived as valuable resources for teachers because they present material in an unusual way, clearly illustrate important relationships, and so forth. The more ideas a book presents and interrelates, the higher its rating.

Activity resource: The greater the quantity and the more readily available a book's material is for immediate student use for classroom activities or individual projects, the higher the rating as an activity resource.

VI = Visual impact
IR = Intellectual rigor
TR = Teacher reference
AR = Activity resource
CH = Discovering Geometry chapter

Book/Description	VI	IR	TR	AR	CH
Abbott, E., *Flatland*, Mineola, NY: Dover Publications, 1884 This science fiction classic about life in a two-dimensional world is a great discussion starter that helps students visualize shapes in one, two, three, and higher dimensions. *Flatland* is also a work of political and social satire.	2	4	4	4	2
Bain, G., *Celtic Art: Methods of Construction*, Mineola, NY: Dover Publications, 1973 A true classic, this large-format paperback is visually impressive. The many hand-drawn illustrations appear authentic to the topic. Clear and intuitive instructions enable even a novice to readily re-create many intricate Celtic borders and knot designs.	5+	3	5	5+	0.6

Book/Description	VI	IR	TR	AR	CH
Beard, Colonel R. S., *Patterns in Space*, Mountain View, CA: Creative Publications, 1973 This amazing exposition of meticulous mathematics has been a classic since its first publication in 1973. Polygons, stars, ellipsoids, spirals, and polyhedrons all undergo Colonel Beard's masterful inspection and analysis. The visuals alone are worth the price.	5+	4	5+	3	0,8, 11
Beyer, J., *The Quilter's Album of Blocks and Borders*, McClean, VA: EPM Publications, 1986 I have found no better resource for organizing the study of quilts as a way to help students plan for a quilt project. The designs are clearly illustrated, and a transparent pattern grid sheet simplifies even complicated designs. The artistic and technical tips are invaluable for even accomplished quilters.	4	2	4	5	
Blackwell, W., *Geometry in Architecture*, Berkeley, CA: Key Curriculum Press, 1984 While exploring the applications of geometry to our built environment, Blackwell offers convincing evidence that geometric principles have an increasing relevance to the design of furniture, buildings, and cities.	5	4	4	2	0,2, 9,10, 11
Boles, M., and Newman, R., *The Golden Relationship—Book 1: Universal Patterns*, Bradford, MA: Pythagorean Press, 1990 From basic geometric constructions through all the special triangles and relationships—including dynamic rectangles, spirals, and the Fibonacci numbers—fine hand-drawn graphics and tantalizing text provide a storehouse of goodies. Even the appendices are outstanding. This volume was followed by . . .	5	5	5+	5	12
Boles, M., and Newman, R., *The Golden Relationship—Book 2: The Surface Plane*, Bradford, MA: Pythagorean Press, 1992 Consistent in format with Book 1, the usefulness and stimulation density of this book are set on max. This volume focuses on grids that subdivide the plane, symmetry, the circle in the plane, the tiling of the plane, fractals, and the manipulation of the "pliable" plane. (Wow, two more books projected for the series? Can't wait!)	5	5	5+	5	
Botermans, J., *Paper Capers*, New York: Henry Holt, 1986 Botermans provides clear directions for producing from paper an impressive variety of clever models, puzzles, and decorations that both intrigue and illustrate exemplary geometry.	5	3	4	5+	8,11
Critchow, K., *Order in Space: A Design Sourcebook*, London: Thames Hudson, 1969 An intensely intellectual and visual presentation that culminates in two incredible "periodic charts": one interrelates the regular and semiregular solids by their properties, the other organizes all space-filling polyhedron combinations.	5	5+	5	1	11
Cundy, H. M., and Rollett, A. P., *Mathematical Models*, London: Oxford University Press, 1961 Although not new, this classic endures because it presents so many models and ideas so well. Included are the usual and many unusual models from plane and solid geometry as well as mechanical linkages and logic machine models.	4	5	5	4	11
Devlin, K., *Mathematics: The Science of Patterns*, New York: Scientific American Library, 1994 (distributed by W. H. Freeman) Attractive and engaging, Devlin's book takes us through history from the ancients to classifying knots, toying with Conway's convex solid that fills space aperiodically, Wiles's proof of Fermat's Last Theorem, and computer graphics. All of these topics are presented to reveal the beauty and powerful utility of pattern.	5	5	5	3	

Book/Description	VI	IR	TR	AR	CH
Dixon, R., *Mathographics*, Mineola, NY: Dover Publications, 1991 *Mathographics* begins with the compass-and-straightedge constructions for "eggs" and goes on to explore a variety of other geometric constructions and concepts. I learned an approximate construction for the regular septagon, how to construct a square approximately equal in area to a given circle, how to construct inversions in a circle, and I was introduced to the involutes of an evolute. In addition to the constructions, this book contains a full section on BASIC programs that produce a wild variety of transformations and some great computer graphics that illustrate these surface manipulations.	5	4	5	4	
Edmondson, A., *A Fuller Explanation: The Synergetic Geometry of R. Buckminster Fuller*, New York: Birkhauser, 1987 This intellectual exposition of many of Bucky Fuller's mathematical excursions is extremely well done. Although not light reading, it does help the reader grasp some very sophisticated and difficult concepts.	3	5	4	2	0,11
El-Said, I., and Parman, A., *Geometric Concepts in Islamic Art*, Palo Alto, CA: Dale Seymour Publications, 1985 A wonderful presentation that descriptively and visually documents the philosophy, geometry, and complexity of Islamic art in a comprehensive and understandable fashion.	5	5	5	5	0.7
Engelhardt, J. (ed), *Geometry in Our World*, Reston, VA: NCTM, 1987 This collection of 200 slides with commentary is organized by themes: points, lines, planes and angles, polygons, polyhedrons, circles, cylinders, spheres and cones, symmetry, tessellations, similarity, and curves. The collection depicts the pervasive nature of these themes in our immediate environment.	5	3	4	3	0.1
Ernst, B., *Adventures with Impossible Figures*, New York: Tarquin Publications, 1986 A fascinating little book that clearly illustrates the joy of creating and toying with the impossible, from Oscar Reutersvarrd's 1934 Triangle through a variety of other types of impossible figures. Students find the ideas stimulating and understandable after little study.	5+	4	5	4	0
Ernst, B., *The Magic Mirror of M. C. Escher*, New York: Ballentine Books, 1976 This is the best choice for an affordable compendium of Escher's planning sketches and finished works. *The Magic Mirror* profusely illustrates the technical skills and the intuitive mathematical genius of the "master of transformations."	5+	5	5	5	8
Feininger, A., *The Anatomy of Nature*, Mineola, NY: Dover Publications, 1956 As shown in this oversized Dover paperback bargain, Feininger is especially skilled at creating photographs that magnificently capture geometric patterns in such natural structures as skulls, flowers, insect faces, and animal tracks in the sand.	5+	2	4	2	0
Fusè, T, *Origami Boxes*, New York: Japan Publications, 1991 (available from Key Curriculum Press) Origami boxes are essentially geometrical. Folding them gives students a great introduction to symmetry (see Lesson 0.1 in *Discovering Geometry*), not to mention a beautiful and useful finished product. These boxes are a little easier to create than most of the models in *Unit Origami* (see below).	5	3	3	5	0,8
Fusè, T, *Unit Origami*, New York: Japan Publications, 1991 (available from Key Curriculum Press) A gorgeous origami book especially for geometry lovers. Fusè gives step-by-step instructions for creating incredible solids, from Platonic and Archimedean solids (with or without their duals peeping through their faces) to "fractalized" stellated octahedrons to rhombitruncated icosidodecahedrons. Paper and classroom guide for using *Unit Origami* is also available from Key Curriculum Press.	5	3	3	5	1,11

Book/Description	VI	IR	TR	AR	CH
Garland, T., *Fascinating Fibonaccis: Mystery and Magic in Numbers*, Palo Alto, CA: Dale Seymour Publications, 1987. Garland finds the frequency of Fibonaccis in natural and theoretical phenomena fascinating, and communicates this with facility.	4	5	5	3	1,12
Ghyka, M., *The Geometry of Art and Life*, Mineola, NY: Dover Publications, 1977. Is there order, harmony, and proportion in life? From the ancient Greeks to the Renaissance artists, Professor Ghyka presents mathematical and mystical ideas on this question.	3	4	4	2	0,12
Grafton, C. B., *Optical Designs in Motion with Moiré Overlays*, Mineola, NY: Dover Publications, 1976. By sliding patterns on clear acetate overlays over a variety of other patterns printed on the pages, the viewer creates some incredibly dynamic illusions. A fascinating activity for all who try it, even if they don't ask "How's that do that?"	5+	1	4	5+	0.4
Greco, C. and S., *Piercing the Surface: X-Rays of Nature*, New York: Harry Abrams, 1986. X-ray photographs of shells, flowers, and insects reveal unbelievable examples of magnificent symmetry in nature. Wonder full!	5+	1	5	2	0
Grunbaum, B., and Shephard, G. C., *Tilings and Patterns, An Introduction*, New York: W. H. Freeman, 1987. A feast for the eyes and the intellect, this book is sure to be classic. Thousands of years and countless cultures are represented and organized in this analysis of two-dimensional pattern.	5+	5+	5+	2	8
Hargittai, I. and M., *Symmetry: A Unifying Concept*, Bolinas, CA: Shelter Publications, 1994. Dense with black and white photos and illustrations from art, nature, and science, this is a symmetry sensitivity training manual. Amplified by clear and simple text, the images in this book include corporate logos, art from around the world, quasicrystals, and much, much more.	5+	3	5+	1	0,8
Hildebrandt, S., and Tromba, A., *Mathematics and Optimal Form*, New York: W. H. Freeman, 1985. Striking photos are combined with compelling text to explore the calculus of optimization: the maximizing or minimizing of materials, forces, area, volume, flow, and so on. The reader is led to appreciate—through examples from atomic nuclei to spiraling galaxies—the principle of economy in nature, which is to proceed in the simplest and most efficient way.	5	5	5	1	0
Hiner, M., *Paper Engineering*, Fireside Books (Simon and Schuster, New York) 1985. A ready-to-go, hands-on minicourse on paper engineering. Everything's here to make paper mechanisms that pop up, slide, and rotate. Fun and instructive. Now you can really appreciate those kiddie pop-up books.	5	3	4	5+	0,6
Hix, K., *Geo-Dynamics*, Calistoga, CA: Crystal Reflections, 1978. Step-by-step instructions for creating geometric models of paper or wooden blocks that flex, twist, or distort in delightful ways.	3	2	3	5	0
Hornung, C. P., *Handbook of Designs and Devices: 1,836 Basic Designs and Their Variations*, Mineola, NY: Dover Publications, 1959. Hornung's Dover classic shows hundreds of designs based on a few simple forms. Great as an example of variations on a theme.	5	2	5	2	0
Huntley, H. E., *The Divine Proportion*, Mineola, NY: Dover Publications, 1970. This book explains the fascinating relationship between geometry and aesthetics. It explores a number of branches of simple mathematics that all lead to new views of the golden section.	3	4	4	2	12

Book/Description	VI	IR	TR	AR	CH
Jacobs, H., *Mathematics—A Human Endeavor*, San Francisco: W.H. Freeman, 1995 With humor and a reader-friendly text that is profusely punctuated with cartoons, photos, and illustrative graphics, Jacobs invites us to play in chapters that include Mathematical Thinking, Mathematical Curves, Regular Polygons, and Some Topics in Topology. Other chapters focus on less geometric but still inviting mathematics. This text is perfect for a math electives course at the high school or undergraduate level.	4	3	5	5	
Jenkins, G., and Wild, A., *Make Shapes: Mathematical Models* (vol 1, 2, and 3), New York: Tarquin Publications, 1985 The series represents a good idea and a good variety of regular, stellated, and other polyhedrons, but the paper provided is a bit too thin to be of practical value in a classroom setting except for the most careful of students.	4	3	4	5	11
Jenkins, G. and Wild, A., *Mathematical Curiosities*, (vol 1, 2, and 3), New York: Tarquin Publications, 1981 As in *Make Shapes: Mathematical Models* (see above), the thinness of the paper is a problem. This series presents a collection of stimulating models that illustrate such mathematical curiosities as shapes of constant width, hexyflexagons, rotating rings, dissections, flip-flop parallelepipeds, and more.	5	2	4	5	11
Kappraff, J., *Connections: The Geometric Bridge Between Art and Science*, New York: McGraw-Hill, 1991 Drawing on the work of Escher, Fuller, Mandelbrot, and Penrose, *Connections* is a rich and stimulating exploration of design science. Care and scholarship are evident throughout, from the historical detailing to the challenging puzzles, classic and new.	5	5+	5+	4	
Kastner, B., *Space Mathematics*, Greenbelt, MD: NASA, 1986 (Order number: 87N15742) Organized by topic, this is a great collection of real-world problems encountered by scientists and engineers when they deal with such space-related issues as vehicular design and best orbits. A treat as a technical but accessible teacher's resource for problems in geometry and trigonometry, probability and statistics, the algebra of conic sections and matrices, exponential and logarithmic functions, and calculus.	3	5	3	4	7,11, 13
Kim, S., *Inversions*, Berkeley, CA: Key Curriculum Press, 1981 An intense illustration of geometry applied to graphic design and calligraphy. The concise explanations and summaries are as exemplary as the concepts behind the images. Scott Kim takes us up, down, and around, only to bring us back to the beginning!	5+	5	5	3	8.3
Lawlor, R., *Sacred Geometry: Philosophy and Practice*, New York: Thames and Hudson, 1982 This fascinating collection of geometric understandings, presented as they were taught and used by the ancients in Egypt, Greece, India, and China, describes the systems of numbers, shapes, and proportions used to describe and determine the forms found in nature and practiced in art, architecture, and design.	5	5	5	3	
Laycock, M., *Bucky for Beginners—SYNERGETIC Geometry*, Hayward, CA: Activity Resources, 1984 Though the illustrations are somewhat simplistic, the design and content of the activities and the models are clear, clever, and cogent. A rich resource for exploring the forms and forces that influence structural integrity.	2	5	5	5	11
Lénárt, I., *Non-Euclidean Adventures on the Lénárt Sphere*, Berkeley, CA: Key Curriculum Press, 1996 A collection of blackline activity masters for doing hands-on non-Euclidean geometry on a sphere. This is a great resource for many of the Take Another Look suggestions in *Discovering Geometry*.	4	5	5	5	

Book/Description	VI	IR	TR	AR	CH
Locher, J. L., *The Infinite World of M. C. Escher*, New York: Harry Abrams, 1984 A typical Abrams art publication: a great variety of studies and works by the artist—some rarely seen elsewhere—that are printed and presented impeccably.	5+	2	5	2	8
Locher, J. L. (ed) *M. C. Escher: His Life and Complete Graphic Work*, New York: Harry Abrams, 1982 The Escher book to end all! Magnificent! But very expensive.	5+	2	5	5	8
Locke, J., *Isometric Perspective Designs and How to Create Them*, Mineola, NY: Dover Publications, 1981 One of three inexpensive large-format Dover Publications that clearly and concisely present a concept (for example, isometric perspective), show how to construct it, and then illustrate variations and elaborations on that basic construction.	4	3	4	5+	0.8
Mandelbrot, B., *The Fractal Geometry of Nature*, New York: W. H. Freeman, 1983 The progenitor of fractal spaces, Mandelbrot describes the natural and mathematical realities that led to the formulation of this whole new field. Some powerful mathematics and spectacular images are included in this treatise. Tough reading beyond the reach of most students.	5	5	5	1	
McKillip, R., *The Celtic Design Book*, Owings Mills, MD: Stemmer House, 1984 McKillip's book is one of many from Stemmer House that detail patterns found in arts and crafts. An introduction complements the beautiful illustrations of people, beasts, birds, and serpents who writhe their way through twisting bands of knotwork.	5	4	4	3	0
McKim, R. H., *Thinking Visually*, Belmont, CA: Lifetime Learning Publications, 1980 McKim's book, one of the first on the topic of thinking visually, is a classic text combining concepts of design, art, and critical thinking. It is an excellent source for challenging visual and conceptual activities.	5	4	5	5	0,2,8
McMorris, P., and Kile, M., *The Art Quilt*, San Francisco: Quilt Digest Press, 1986 Quilts made by 17 leading quiltmakers for this landmark book are the focus of a fascinating, in-depth look at this century's quiltmaking movement and the emergence of the contemporary quilt.	5	2	4	2	0,8,9
Meehan, A., *Celtic Design: A Beginner's Manual*, New York: Thames and Hudson, 1994 Beautifully illustrated with images and calligraphy, this is the first of a series of Thames and Hudson books focused on the patterns and art of the Celts. Freehand and canonical methods of creating the Celtic step, key, and spiral patterns are wonderfully detailed in this book, as are step-by-step methods for creating illustrated manuscripts and decorative letters in the Celtic tradition. Other books in the series focus on knotwork, illuminated letters and animals, and spiral and maze patterns.	4	2	5	5	0.6
Miyazaki, K., *An Adventure in Multidimensional Space: Art & Geometry of Polygons, Polyhedra & Polytopes*, New York: Wiley, 1986 Magnificent models and renderings colorfully captivate the viewer and provide an essay that is intuitively understandable. The text, though somewhat disjointed, draws together a wealth of historical information and is presented through such creative correlations as the Circle by Pythagoras, the Cosmos by Plato, the Dream by Kepler, Synergy by Fuller, the Labyrinth by Möbius, Magic by Dürer, the Planet by Penrose, the Crystal by Schlafli, the Creation by Coxeter, and the Hypersphere by Einstein.	5+	5	5	1	0,11
Moscovich, I., *Mindbenders: Games of Chance*, New York: Random House, 1986 Great geometry, great challenge, great fun, great games, great as a source of activities for students working alone, in pairs, or in small groups. Visually dense and dazzling.	5	2	5	5	4–16

Book/Description	VI	IR	TR	AR	CH
National Wildlife Federation, *Patterns in the Wild*, Washington, DC: National Wildlife Federation, 1992 Bringing together the most striking color photos from *National Wildlife* magazine, this portfolio of the world's leading nature photographers captures the startling beauty of spirals, stripes, circles, branches, rays, and repeating shapes in natural forms.	5+	1	5	1	0
Neill, W., and Murphy, P., *By Nature's Design*, San Francisco: Chronicle Books, 1993 With poetic prose, astute mathematical explanations, and incredible images of natural phenomena, we are taken on a magical mystery tour of spirals and helixes; meanders and ripples; spheres and explosions; branching, packing, and cracking; and fractals. Truly, as expressed in Diane Ackerman's forward, "(Patterns) are visually succulent. The mind savors them. It is a kind of comfort food. Feast here on some of the wonders in nature's pantry."	5+	4	5	1	0
NC School of Science and Math, *Geometric Probability: New Topics for Secondary School Mathematics*, Reston, VA: NCTM, 1988 *Geometric Probability* shows students familiar mathematics in new contexts and exposes them to creative, sometimes surprising, applications. This book provides an introduction to mathematical modeling, computer simulations, and the distinction between discrete and continuous phenomena. Includes an IBM-PC compatible disk.	1	5	3	3	4–16
O'Brien, J., *How to Design by Accident*, Mineola, NY: Dover Publications, 1968 Doing these activities takes some time and preparation, but the results clearly illustrate the geometry of flow, expansion, contraction, and so on. Surprisingly aesthetic creations are readily generated by most explorers.	4	3	4	5	0
Oliver, J., *Polysymmetrics*, New York: Tarquin Publications, 1979 With just a few basic but powerful design concepts and simple constructions, students can readily develop an infinite variety of designs, many of which are delightfully and surprisingly complex.	4	3	4	5+	8
Parramon, J. M., *Perspective*, Los Angeles: HP Books, 1981 An excellent and understandable introduction to one-, two-, and three-point perspective. Appeals on artistic and geometric levels.	5	4	5	5	0.8
Pearce, P., *Structure in Nature Is a Strategy for Design*, Cambridge, MA: MIT Press, 1978 Spirals, meanders, junctions, branching—these are all wonderfully described and illustrated in this early Pearce classic that combines nature, mathematics, science, and aesthetics.	4	5	5	1	0
Pearce, P. and S., *Polyhedra Primer*, Palo Alto, CA: Dale Seymour Publications, 1985 A terrific resource for anyone interested in studying polyhedrons. The organization and clear blackline illustrations make it all understandable despite the maze of multisyllabic monikers.	5	5	5+	3	11.1
Peitgen, H. O., *The Beauty of Fractals*, New York: Springer-Verlag, 1986 Beautiful, indeed, are the images. The explanations and organization make this particularly useful to the interested teacher, though this book is beyond most high school students.	5	5	5	2	
Pentagram Design Limited, *Pentagames*, Fireside Books (Simon and Schuster, New York), 1990 Same wonderfully stimulating "aura" as its predecessor, listed below, this new collection of pencil-and-paper games, word games, card games, sleights-of-hand, paper-folding and string games, and more are delightful. Watch out for falling egos and Mensa braggers.	5+	3	4	5	
Pentagram Design Limited, *Puzzlegrams*, Fireside Books (Simon and Schuster, New York), 1988 Bold and colorful graphics in a beautifully designed format make both the classic and new games and puzzles a real treat for the eye and intellect. Hey, no peeking at the answers in less than 15 minutes of "wait time"!	5+	3	4	5	

Book/Description	VI	IR	TR	AR	CH
Peterson, I., *The Mathematical Tourist: Snapshots of Modern Mathematics*, New York: W. H. Freeman, 1988 Peterson elucidates such recent mathematical peculiarities as finding primes, fractal excursions, delving into different dimensions, describing chaos, creating cryptosystems, and topographic transmographications.	5	5	5	2	
Pohl, V., *Enrich Geometry Using String Designs*, Reston, VA: NCTM, 1986 This inexpensive book profusely illustrates the enrichment symmography can provide. The ideas are classroom tested and do work to generate interest and investigation.	4	3	4	5+	0.2
Posamentier, A., and Sheridan, G., *Math Motivators! Investigations in Geometry*, Palo Alto, CA: Addison-Wesley, 1982 A great collection of over 30 investigations that probe such topics as problems of antiquity, post- and non-Euclidean geometry, solid geometry, and geometric applications and puzzles. Each investigation is self-contained and includes a blackline master as well as teacher's notes. Great for enrichment and student projects.	3	4	5	5+	
Ranucci, E., *Seeing Shapes*, Mountain View, CA: Creative Publications, 1973 The emphasis of most of the exercises in this book is visualization, usually from differing perspectives. The exercises—most are not unique but are presented well—range in difficulty and cover such categories as orthographic and isometric drawings, paper folding and cutting, reflections, and tessellations.	3	2	4	5	0,8
Read, R. C., *Tangrams—330 Puzzles*, Mineola, NY: Dover Publications, 1965 This tried-and-true collection consists of tangram picture puzzles and their solutions. Simple and straightforward.	3	2	4	5	10.6
Rucker, R., *Mindtools*, Boston: Houghton Mifflin, 1987 The tools Rucker so playfully and yet precisely describes are the "five levels or modes of thought": number, space, logic, infinity, and information. While not light reading, his affable style and patient development of his lectures make some very incomprehensible concepts very approachable.	3	5	5	1	1,14
Scharf, D., *Magnifications*, New York: Schocken Books, 1977 Scharf focuses his scanning electron microscope on a variety of living and nonliving things to create some unbelievable landscapes, clearly illustrating some obvious natural regularities.	5	3	4	2	0
Schattschneider, D., *Visions of Symmetry*, New York: W. H. Freeman, 1991 The definitive source on the mathematics of Escher's tessellation drawings. *Visions* tells the fascinating story of the artist's discovery of the world of geometry. Contains more than 350 illustrations, 180 of which had not been published previously.	5+	5+	3	2	0,8
Schattschneider, D., and Walker, W., *M. C. Escher Kaleidocycles*, Corte Madera, CA: Pomegranate Artbooks, 1987 A wonderful remake of the original, this construction kit allows students to create a variety of polyhedrons and manipulable objects decorated by Escher art. This is a top-quality product with a workable and durable weight stock, good art reproduction, and excellent directions and background materials.	5+	5	5	5+	8,11
Schneider, M., *A Beginner's Guide to Constructing the Universe*, New York: HarperCollins, 1994 Modern science seems to be reaffirming the ancient belief that a consistent language underpins every level of the universe, from atoms to galaxies. Schneider translates that eloquent language into lyrical prose documented by hundreds of eye-opening photos and images. Each of the numbers 1 through 10 has its own chapter, and each chapter is a cornucopia crammed with an abundance of its number's historic, mythological, arithmetic, geometric, and philosophic aspects. Throughout the book, sidebar quotes, illustrations, and factoids keep the reader as stimulated as MTV does ($M \neq$ "math"). This book is a hearty feast for the eyes, mind, and soul.	5+	5	5+	5+	

Book/Description	VI	IR	TR	AR	CH
Senechal, M., and Fleck, G., *Shaping Space—A Polyhedral Approach*, New York: Birkhauser, 1988 — Inspired by the Shaping Space Conference, held in April 1984 at Smith College, this exuberant book explores facets of polyhedral history, theory, and omnipresence in natural and designed forms. In an amazing array of articles from science, engineering, classroom applications, and creative envisioning, geometry's centrality to human consciousness is clearly demonstrated.	5+	5+	5	4	11
Seymour, D., *Geometric Design*, Palo Alto, CA: Dale Seymour Publications, 1988 — A pleasure to use with students in developing construction skills. The book features geometric designs and shows the easy-to-follow construction sequences required to produce them.	5	3	5	5	0,8
Seymour, D., *Visual Patterns in Pascal's Triangle*, Palo Alto, CA: Dale Seymour Publications, 1986 — A collection of Pascal's triangle patterns that can be torn out and used for bulletin board display together with problems for students.	4	3	4	4	1
Seymour, D., and Britton, J., *Introduction to Tessellations*, Palo Alto, CA: Dale Seymour Publications, 1985 — Another excellent Dale Seymour resource book that develops many concepts related to tessellations through activities and thoughtful dialog. I think this is the best book on the topic at the secondary level.	5	4	5	4	8
Seymour, D., and Shedd, M., *Finite Differences*, Palo Alto, CA: Dale Seymour Publications, 1973 — Explains the problem-solving technique called finite differences. A useful companion to the *Discovering Geometry* lessons on inductive reasoning and number patterns.	1	4	5	4	1
Seymour, D., Silvey, L., and Snider, J., *Line Designs*, Mountain View, CA: Creative Publications, 1974 — A pattern and instruction book for "curve stitching," this book contains perforated pages that can be reproduced as student worksheets.	4	1	3	5	0.2
Slocum, J., and Botermans, J., *Puzzles Old and New*, Seattle, WA: University of Washington Press, 1988 — A lavishly illustrated collection of a dazzling array of puzzles from many cultures and periods. Presents both the challenges and the solutions. A real treat.	5+	5	5	4	
Smith, A. G., *Cut and Assemble 3-D Shapes*, Mineola, NY: Dover Publications, 1986 — Although the stock is a bit thinner than is practical, the nets are colorful and accurate. Some very good models can be made by the careful student.	4	1	5	5	11
Smith, S., *Agnesi to Zeno*, Berkeley, CA: Key Curriculum Press, 1995 — One of the best history-of-math books around. Each of over 100 vignettes is easily accessible for students, and each includes activities to engage students in the mathematics presented in the vignette. Beautifully illustrated.	5	5	5	5	
Sparke, P., et al, *Design Source Book*, Secaucus, NJ: Chartwell Books, 1987 — A visual treat that shows a vast collection of the important design classics and styles of the last 100 years, including arts and crafts, art nouveau, the "machine" aesthetic, art deco, streamlining, consumerism, modernism, and today's high tech.	5+	4	5	2	0,8
Steierlin, E. (ed), *The Spirit of Colors*, Cambridge, MA: MIT Press, 1981 — The colorful and careful design and artwork of Karl Gestetner is featured in this volume. Much geometry is immediately obvious, and even more is evident through some excellent explanation.	5	3	4	2	0
Steinhaus, H., *Mathematical Snapshots*, London: Oxford University Press, 1969 — Originally published in 1950, Steinhaus's book still stretches our understanding and abilities. The majority of these challenging topics deal directly with geometry and require no formal mathematics training beyond the high school level.	3	5	5	3	

Book/Description	VI	IR	TR	AR	CH
Stevens, P., *Handbook of Regular Patterns*, Cambridge, MA: MIT Press, 1981 Stevens defines a scheme of a mere 34 generalized categories into which all designs can be classified. Imagine, just 34 archetypes! Offered as examples are hundreds of designs from cultures throughout history and around the globe.	5+	5	5+	2	0
Stevens, P., *Patterns in Nature*, Boston: Little and Brown, 1974 In a startling synthesis of art and science, Stevens uses hundreds of photos and illustrations to examine such apparently universal design themes as spirals, meanders, branching and exploding patterns, and their natural evolution as consequences of the laws of stress, flow, turbulence, least effort, surface tension, close packing, and the constraints of three-dimensional space.	4	5	5	2	
Stonerod, D., *Puzzles in Space*, Hayward, CA: Activity Resources, 1982 Activities such as dissections and the determination of volumetric relationships are explored using the Platonic solids and other solids such as the cuboctahedron and the rhombic dodecahedron.	3	3	5	5	11
Sykes, M, *Source Book of Problems for Geometry*, Palo Alto, CA: Dale Seymour Publications, 1912 (reprint) A collection of constructions and mathematical relationships in tiled and parquet floor designs, medieval stained glass and tracery panel designs, and trusses and arches. Clearly communicates the geometric nature of the art and architecture of these powerful works.	3	5	5	2	
Taniuchi, T., *Paper Sculpture*, Tokyo: Genkosha, 1985 Contains the directions, photos, and preprinted card stock needed to create about a dozen nice, finished sculptures, hangings, and more. A good eye and a very careful hand with a sharp blade is required to really produce the sculptures as shown in the book.	5	2	3	5	
Turner, H., *Triad Optical Illusions and How to Design Them*, Mineola, NY: Dover Publications, 1978 Another large-format Dover paperback that can stimulate hours of creative construction projects.	4	3	4	5+	0.4
van Delft, P., and Botermans, J., *Creative Puzzles of the World*, Berkeley, CA: Key Curriculum Press, 1995 A precursor to Slocum's *Puzzles Old and New*, this book is as visually and puzzlingly exciting. Truly captivating mathematics here!	5+	4	5	3	
Vasarely, V., *Vasarely*, New York: Alpine Fine Arts Collection, 1978 This is but one of many collections of Vasarely graphics. It, like the other collections, is a visual marvel. Although Vasarely books are expensive, consider treating yourself and your students to one. Shop around and find your favorite. Look in used bookstores.	5+	3	4	2	0
Visual Geometry Project, *The Platonic Solids Activity Book*, Berkeley, CA: Key Curriculum Press, 1991 A well-crafted collection of blackline masters for 11 activities and 14 student projects. All lead to insights and discoveries about regular and nonregular polyhedrons, 3-D symmetry, space packing, duality, and Euler's formula. Accompanied by dazzling computer-animated videos and a manipulative kit with sufficient die-cut pieces for an entire class to build models of these and other solids.	5	5	5	5+	11
Visual Geometry Project, *The Stella Octangula Activity Book*, Berkeley, CA: Key Curriculum Press, 1991 Blackline masters for 9 activities and 12 student projects, each guiding inquiry into this simple but elegant stellated octahedron. Accompanied by dazzling computer-animated videos and a manipulative kit.	5	5	5	5+	11
Visual Geometry Project, *Three-Dimensional Symmetry Activity Book*, Berkeley, CA: Key Curriculum Press, 1995 This collection of activities makes an otherwise hard-to-teach topic come alive for students. The accompanying video and manipulative kit ensure that students get the visual and hands-on experience necessary to fully grasp two- and three-dimensional symmetry concepts. The same manipulative kit is used for the Visual Geometry Project's *The Platonic Solids*, listed above.	5	5	5	5+	0.8

Book/Description	VI	IR	TR	AR	CH
Walter, M., *The Mirror Puzzle Book*, New York: Tarquin Publications, 1985 This is a small booklet of reflectional symmetry puzzles. Working through the puzzles students sharpen their visual-thinking skills and have fun at the same time. This booklet should be on every geometry teacher's desk, available for students to pick up and play with.	4	3	3	5	0,8
Wells, D., *The Penguin Dictionary of Curious and Interesting Geometry*, New York: Penguin Books, 1991 A century or two of play in this collection of figures, theorems, patterns, properties, and geometric gems. I don't know where else you can find the Appolonian gasket, Dandelin spheres, the Euler line, Fatou dust, Fermat points, interlocking polyminoes, Poncelet's porism, the Vodenberg tessellation, and the unilluminable room all in one volume.	4	5	5	2	
Williams, R., *The Geometrical Foundation of Natural Structure*, Mineola, NY: Dover Publications, 1979 The strength of this book is its marvelous explanations of the interrelationships among different tessellations and space figures using duals, packing spheres, and rotation-translation operations. Dense with data and charts.	3	5	5+	1	0,8
Wills, H., *Leonardo's Dessert—No Pi*, Reston, VA: NCTM, 1985 A short and small NCTM publication that develops many ideas by playing with a very simple basic construction.	3	4	4	2	7,9,10
Wilson, J., *Mosaic and Tessellated Patterns—How to Create Them*, Mineola, NY: Dover Publications, 1983 This large-format Dover paperback explores the basic organizing principles of tiling patterns and many resulting tessellations.	4	3	5	4	8
Zhang, W., *Exploring Math Through Puzzles*, Berkeley, CA: Key Curriculum Press, 1996 Blackline master activities show how to make 54 puzzles out of string, beads, and other simple, cheap items. Students unlock the secrets of many puzzle types by exploring the mathematics behind them. A convenient, economical kit accompanies the book.	5	5	5	5	

Geometry Manipulatives, Puzzles, and Toys

The manipulatives, puzzles, and toys listed here are evaluated on a scale from 5+ (high) to 1 (low) for the following criteria: sensory appeal, value as a heuristic device to stimulate inquisitive response, and the most effective group size for each item's use. The list is not exhaustive. It is suggestive of the kinds of playthings you might want to keep in your classroom, use in group settings sporadically, or both.

Sensory appeal: The sensory appeal of an item includes such characteristics as color, heft, surface texture, "fit and finish," and so on. The nicer an item's look and feel and the more "user friendly" it is, the higher its rating.

Heuristic value: This category denotes how useful an item is for illustrating mathematical relationships or for generating investigation opportunities. Highly rated items are often startling, subtle, perplexing, or allow students to build patterns or structures.

Group size: Many of the items are flexible enough that they lend themselves to individual or small-group work. The construction manipulatives work best in a classroom setting when each student has access to enough pieces to build something significant. Most manipulatives are effectively used with some guided inquiry, such as general questions or a suggested sequence of explorations. Puzzles are most effectively used by individuals and without much explanation.

Note: The list of suppliers in the chart is not exhaustive. Check the catalogs of your favorite school suppliers to see whether they also carry these items.

SA = Sensory appeal
HV = Heuristic value
GS = Group size
COST = Approximate cost range

Item/Description	Supplier	SA	HV	GS	COST
Exploring Math Through Puzzles Kit Designed to accompany the book *Exploring Math Through Puzzles* by Wei Zhang (see the Bibliography). Contains enough beads, rings, string, cubes, and puzzle boards to make 54 puzzles. By actually making the puzzles, students unlock their secrets. And there may be no more economical way to supply your classroom with puzzles!	Key Curriculum Press	5+	5	1–4	<$30
Geo D-Stix Thin plastic rods of varying lengths are joined by five, six, and eight sleeve connectors to form figures. Although the space figures are easy to produce and relationships are clearly visualized, the connectors are the system's flaw: they easily rip when a little force is applied to a model, and the sleeves rip off frequently when models are disassembled. *D-Stix* have been around quite a while, but other construction systems are far more durable.	Creative Publications, Dale Seymour Publications, Educational Teaching Aids (ETA)	4	4	1–6	<$25

Item/Description	Supplier	SA	HV	GS	COST
Geometric Plastic Models Beautiful and visually powerful, most of these 15 acrylic models have internal dissection plates that enhance the visualization of diagonals, altitudes, central angles, radii, and so on. Nine of the models have apertures for easy filling and volume comparison. These are quite expensive but stunning.	Cuisenaire Company	5+	5	1–6	$195
GeoMorph 12 Designed by the talented Yoshimata, students can transform this rotating ring of tetrahedrons into many appealing forms. Good quality plastic provides excellent durability, and the color, heft, and sound seem to be sensually appealing.	Binary Arts Corporation	5	3	1	<$25
Googolplex The *Googolplex* pieces are regular triangles, squares, and pentagons as open frames and plates, so designs or structures can appear "skeletal" or have planar faces. The pieces are joined by small connectors that form strong hinges and thus strong models. Holes for joining struts to the midpoints of the edges or to the centroids of the faces give *Googolplex* flexibility as a teaching device. Teacher resource books are available for K–6 and 7–12.	Creative Publications, Dale Seymour Publications	5+	5+	1–3	<$75
Gordian Knot Previously available as *Looney Loop*, this topological puzzle appears in *Puzzles Old and New* and *Creative Puzzles of the World*. A string appears to be strung around a central bar, but a series of simple manipulations through four closed loops disengages the string and engages most people's disbelief!	Dale Seymour Publications	4	4	1	<$25
Lénárt Sphere Construction Materials Imagine your students being able to work hands-on with spherical geometry! The *Lénárt Sphere's* 8" clear plastic spheres—along with the spherical compass, straightedge, and transparencies—allow for actual investigations that are impossible for most students to even visualize. The *Lénárt Sphere* really brings non-Euclidean proof out of the closet. Great support materials are available.	Key Curriculum Press	5	5	1–4	$60 (basic), $400 (class)
M. C. Escher Kaleidocycles The kaleidocycles are figures students construct from punch-outs. The models require some skill and patience to make, but they are attractive and intriguing once students are on a "roll." The 60-page booklet included is excellent.	Dale Seymour Publications	5+	5	1–3	$19
OCTAbug A fascinating model that students build from die-cut heavy paper triangles, connected with flexible joints, that oscillates among three polyhedral forms: octahedron, icosahedron, and cuboctahedron. An instruction booklet is included.	Design Science Toys, Dale Seymour Publications	5+	4	1–3	<$8
Pattern Blocks In my opinion, no manipulative gives your more "bang for the buck" than this classic. Students actively explore symmetry, patterns, tessellations, angle measurement, area, perimeter relationships, fractional parts, and more. Includes a number of good related teacher resource books.	Cuisenaire, Dale Seymour Publications, Creative Publications, ETA	5+	5+	1–3	<$25
Patty Paper Geometry Michael Serra does it again! With patty papers (you know, the thin waxed paper that separates hamburger patties) it's amazing how easily and quickly your students can explore all the basic Euclidean constructions. The patty papers come in boxes of 1,000, and a great teacher's book and student workbook are available.	Key Curriculum Press	5+	5+	1–3	$6

Item/Description	Supplier	SA	HV	GS	COST
PENTABlocks — A whole new family of pattern blocks that differ from the "classics": the *PENTABlocks* are based on a 36° angle. Students can do the same types of explorations they do with the classic blocks, but many of the results are surprisingly and excitingly different. These blocks provide concrete exploration of the "golden" relationship and self-similarity.	Cuisenaire	5	5+	1–5	$25
Platonic Solids Manipulative Kit — The *Platonic Solids Manipulative Kit* contains eight sets of die-cut panels, rubber bands, straws, and acetate cubes—everything a class needs to build models of the Platonic solids (or any other solids made from regular polygons) and complete the activities in *The Platonic Solids Activity Book*. Serves double-duty as a kit for the *Three-Dimensional Symmetry Activity Book*. Videos also accompany this hands-on manipulative series.	Key Curriculum Press	5	4	1–3	<$50
Polydron — The increase of *Polydron* shapes has made this a much more valuable manipulative for exploring both tessellations and polyhedrons. The pieces come in four colors and are based on a common unit of length (7 cm). Shapes include isosceles triangles, regular triangles, squares, pentagons, hexagons, octagons, and various rhombuses. Many pieces are offered as a frame, with a hole or as a solid face. Pieces join at the edge with a "hinge," although there are also struts and swivel joints. Though its hinging system is less flexible and weaker than it is in *Googolplex*, *Polydron* is easier to work with and forms very attractive models of plane tessellations and three-dimensional figures. The Polydron Protractor, which measures dihedral angles, is ingenious. A teacher's guide is available.	Activity Resources, Creative Publications, Dale Seymour Publications, ETA	5+	5	1–3	<$75
Power Solids — A set of 12 solids that are just the right size for small group explorations of volume. Each solid has an aperture and a removable lid so that it can be filled with water, rice, sand, and so on.	Cuisenaire	5	5	1–3	$17
Reflect-It — You can buy two cosmetic mirrors and tape them together with duct tape, or you can buy the *Reflect-It* mirror. In addition to the large plastic, hinged mirrors, a plastic base with corresponding pairs of positions organizes student explorations. A clearly written teacher's guide is available.	Cuisenaire	5	5	1–4	$6
Soma (and related items) — This classic puzzle created by Swedish mathematician Piet Hein (same fellow with the funny quotes in *Discovering Geometry*) is made by gluing 27 small wooden cubes together. This 3″ cube version is museum quality, in maple and walnut, with precision fit. Design Science Toys also offers other models based on rhombic hexahedrons. Some have interlocking parts or magnets. All Design Science's products exhibit the best fit and finish available.	Design Science Toys	5+	4	1–2	$13
Sphere Pyramid — Two puzzles in one. These plastic spheres come grouped in configurations of two to four spheres each—six shapes in all. With proper stacking they form a regular pyramid or a rectangular pyramid. The first puzzle has only one solution; the second has three.	Dale Seymour Publications	5	4	1–2	<$5
Symmetrics Kits — High quality plastic and appropriately beveled edges make it relatively easy to produce accurate models of a number of Platonic and more interesting solids.	Dale Seymour Publications	3	5	1–2	<$25

Item/Description	Supplier	SA	HV	GS	COST
Synergy Ball Students explore the dynamic properties of tension and compression with a 30 strut tensegrity structure they build. The die-cut card stock pieces have locking tabs for easy assembly. An instruction booklet is included.	Design Science Toys	4	4	1–2	<$5
Tangrams Available in many levels of quality, the seven pieces of this classic puzzle can be combined to form a square or many easy-to-make figures that are more imaginative or suggestive. Many resource materials are available to use with the *Tangrams*.	Cuisenaire, Dale Seymour, Creative Publications, ETA	3	5	1–2	<$1
Tavern Puzzles The fact that they are hand-formed, made of heavy wrought iron, and come in a number of historically certified forms make these puzzles special. The simpler ones—*Conestoga Playmate, Shackled Rings,* and *Iron Maiden*—are solvable by most who are patient. The clanging sound and heft of *Tavern Puzzles* are very appealing to kids of all ages.	Tucker-Jones House	5	4	1	<$25
Tensegritoy (and *Strik-trix*) Though the instructions for the more complex forms get a bit cumbersome, the design and quality of the construction elements are excellent. As the included explanation describes so well, tensegrity is why natural structures resist coming apart. The models provide powerful analogies and can really take a beating.	Design Science Toys	5	5	1–2	$30
Tessellation Exploration Tiles This manipulative is especially valuable in helping students perceive tessellations that are beyond the configurations of simple convex polygons. Many of the ten different tiles offer an unusual, but historically important, variation on basic geometric constructions.	Creative Publications	4	5	1–6	<$50
Three-Dimensional Symmetry Manipulative Kit This kit serves double-duty, with pieces that can be used with *The Three-Dimensional Symmetry Activity Book* and *The Platonic Solids Activity Book.*	Key Curriculum Press	5	4	1–3	<$50
Tower of Hanoi Puzzle This classic puzzle is the basis of the project Three Peg Puzzle, found in Chapter 1 of *Discovering Geometry.* Commercial versions of this puzzle abound, but it is easy to make your own. You could ask a student to take on the DG project, make a version of the puzzle in a woodshop, and donate the product to the class.	Dale Seymour Publications	4	5	1–2	<$15
Two-Piece Pyramid Puzzle Two congruent wooden shapes that form a regular tetrahedron when placed together properly. This is a commercial version of the puzzle that appears in Build a Two-Piece Puzzle, a *Discovering Geometry* Improving Visual Thinking Skills puzzle.	Dale Seymour Publications	4	4	1–2	<$10
Vector Flexor Described by Bucky Fuller as the "vector equilibrium jitterbug," *Vector Flexor* models many natural forces basic to the structure of matter. A cuboctahedron constructed of colorful sticks and flexible rubber connectors, this manipulative has proved to be interesting and indestructible for classroom use.	TOBI Toys	4	4	1	<$25
Visual Thinking Cards Available in two sets of 100 cards each (set *A* is bit easier than set *B*). Activities give students practice in spatial perception and visual discrimination. The perception skills illustrated by the challenges include congruence, directionality or order, illusions, patterns, and symmetry.	Dale Seymour Publications	5	4	1–4	<$50

Item/Description	Supplier	SA	HV	GS	COST
Wei and Stan's Puzzle Selections Renowned puzzlists Wei Zhang and Stan Isaacs have chosen a wide selection of great puzzles for the classroom. See Key Curriculum Press's catalog of mathematics materials for details.	Key Curriculum Press	5	5	1–3	
Zometool This is the most sophisticated mathematical modeling kit available. The 31 zone connectors accept each of 3 different types of color- and shape-coordinated struts, each in 3 coordinated lengths. The resulting possibilities for modeling include nearly all regular polytopes; Penrose tilings and quasi-crystals; two-, three- and four-dimensional golden sections; hypercube arrays; and fractals. Although the plastic and moldings are of excellent quality, you do need to be sure that all struts are *firmly* in place, especially with the more complicated models.	Zometool	5+	5	1–3	<$90

Geometry Tools, Devices, Videos, and Posters

A note about technology

About 6,000 years ago, geometry stimulated the first mathematical technology: the compass. Since then, geometry has merged with computer technology to bring us "Son of Compass": The Geometer's Sketchpad®. Available from Key Curriculum Press, this incredible and fully dynamic software is the most effective I know of for exploring school geometry. In my opinion, it simply cannot be beat as a tool for illustrating, investigating, and communicating geometric relationships. The newest version extends its capabilities to truly integrate coordinate systems, animations, and scripting in such useful and powerful ways that it will change *forever* how I teach geometry. Really!

Sketchpad™ support materials include an exemplary user guide, a reference manual, and teaching notes—these come with the software—*Exploring Geometry with The Geometer's Sketchpad*, and terrific add-on modules for exploring such specific topics as perspective drawing, circle geometry, Pythagorean theorem proofs and problems, conic sections, and trigonometry.

Sketchpad is a natural tool for many investigations in *Discovering Geometry*. Now Sketchpad activities created specifically for students using *Discovering Geometry* are available in *Discovering Geometry with The Geometer's Sketchpad* and in this *Teacher's Resource Book*.

The tools and devices listed below are also extremely useful. The right geometry tools will make presenting geometry easier and more effective—just as the right tools facilitate many other life tasks—and we believe the items listed below will make exploring and experiencing geometry more pleasing for both teachers and students.

Note: The list of suppliers in the chart is not exhaustive. Check the catalogs of your favorite school suppliers to see whether they also carry these items.

Student tools

Item/Description	Supplier
CircleMaster Compass This is an excellent compass. It holds all types of pencils and pens and its setting stays firm during use. The pencil and compass tips can be retracted for safe storage.	Key Curriculum Press, others
Plastic Protractor Plastic protractor makes smaller angles that appear in text easier to measure.	Key Curriculum Press, others
Plastic Ruler Includes both metric and English measures.	Key Curriculum Press, others
Clear Plastic Straightedge A straightedge that doesn't include measurement markings reinforces the concept of geometric constructions. Students are not tempted to measure segments to duplicate them.	Key Curriculum Press, others

Item/Description	Supplier
Patty Papers Perhaps the world's cheapest manipulative and a must for streamlined *Discovering Geometry* investigations.	Key Curriculum Press, others
Perelli-Pak 20 Color-Coded Compass Constructions After students have discovered the basic constructions, these color-coded constructions help them get organized.	Dale Seymour Publications
Safe-T Compass This great inexpensive and safe compass is nonbreakable and easy to use with any pencil or pen. An overhead version of this product is also available.	Safe-T Products
Triman Compass The advantage of this compass is that it has no pointed tip and it doubles as a small ruler. A clear plastic version for effective use on the overhead is available.	Cuisenaire, Creative Publications, Delta Education, others

Teacher/classroom tools

Item/Description	Supplier
Chalkboard Rule, Compass, and Protractor A set of these chalkboard tools is indispensable.	Cuisenaire, Dale Seymour Publications, Creative Publications, Delta Education
Geoboard Set Useful at the beginning of the year for introducing new terms and again later as a model for demonstrating area and perimeter relationships.	Creative Publications, Nasco, Cuisenaire, ETA, Delta Education
Geometric Shapes Tracer A plastic template makes creating your own review sheets, quizzes, and tests easier and clearer.	Creative Publications, Delta Education
Overhead Geoboard Useful for the teacher or student who wishes to demonstrate geoboard discoveries to the entire class.	Creative Publications, Nasco, ETA, Delta Education
Pattern Blocks / Pattern Blocks for the Overhead In my opinion, no manipulative gives you more "bang for the buck" than this classic. You might use it to explore symmetry, patterns, tessellations, angle measurement, area and perimeter relationships, fractional parts, and more. This product is supported by a number of good related teacher resource books.	Cuisenaire, Dale Seymour Publications, Creative Publications, ETA, Delta Education
SAGE Kit–Student Applied Geometry Experiments Students explore and model the intersection of planes, in various orientations, with seven different solids. This kit really helps students who have difficulty visualizing, especially with altitudes. Students can also explore volume with the models.	Nasco
Tessellation Tracer Students can use this plastic template of the regular polygons to create semiregular tessellations, and it helps you and your students create more exacting tessellations of regular polygons. It is also useful on the overhead.	Creative Publications
TesselMania! Using the basic transformations of translation, rotation, and glide reflection, and this software's simple paint and stamp tools, students easily create attractive tessellations. This MECC software is user-friendly and invites play at many meaningful levels. Includes a book of blackline masters geared toward the secondary classroom.	Key Curriculum Press

Item/Description	Supplier
Trundle Wheel	Nasco, Cuisenaire, Delta Education

The trundle wheel is useful in *Discovering Geometry*'s Chapter 7: Circles as an application of the circumference/diameter relationship, and in Chapter 12: Similarity and Chapter 13: Trigonometry for measuring distances too long for meter sticks. One good trundle wheel can also be used as a model for a class project in which students build trundle wheels.

Item/Description	Supplier
Volume Relationships Plastic Models	Cuisenaire, Nasco, Delta Education

Save time by using these models—rather than building your own—to discover the one-third relationship between pyramids and prisms and between cylinders and cones.

Classroom posters

Item/Description	Supplier
Fibonacci Numbers in Nature	Dale Seymour Publications
Geometry By Design	Dale Seymour Publications
Geometry By Nature	Dale Seymour Publications
Geometry Problems One Step Beyond	Dale Seymour Publications
The Golden Proportion	Dale Seymour Publications
M. C. Escher posters	Dale Seymour Publications, poster stores
Math of Africa	Key Curriculum Press
Math of Arabia	Key Curriculum Press
Math of Architecture posters	Creative Publications
Math of China	Key Curriculum Press
Math of Egypt	Key Curriculum Press
Math of Europe	Key Curriculum Press
Math of India	Key Curriculum Press
Math of Japan	Key Curriculum Press
Math of Korea	Key Curriculum Press
Math of Mexico	Key Curriculum Press
Math in Nature	Creative Publications
Math of the Navajo	Key Curriculum Press
Math of Russia	Key Curriculum Press
Math of the United States	Key Curriculum Press
Polyhedra posters	Dale Seymour Publications

Item/Description	Supplier
Quilt posters	Creative Publications
Scott Kim posters	Dale Seymour Publications
Stained Glass Tessellation posters	Creative Publications
Vasarely posters	Dale Seymour Publications, poster stores

Videos

Though rarely used in the mathematics classroom, videos offer another means for visualizing relationships. Each of the videos described below contains enough content and visual impact to justify the use of instructional time on task.

Item/Description (Running time)	Supplier
Donald In Mathemagic Land (27 min)	Walt Disney mini-classic

Full of subtle humor and nice connections, there's enough geometric content to make this classic worth showing. It's okay to not take it too seriously.

The Invisible World (60 min)	National Geographic Video

A truly spectacular journey that explores events the human eye cannot perceive because they are too fast, too slow, too big, too small, or beyond the visible spectrum. The images are incredible and startling in this National Geographic classic.

NOVA: The Shape of Things (60 min)	Vestron Video

Nature's design ethic is based on the efficient use of energy and materials. This translates to the repeated appearance in natural forms of circles and spheres, polygons and polyhedrons, spirals and coils, meanders, and branching. In the process of exploring these natural forms, *The Shape of Space* integrates mathematics and science. Great visuals but the script is a bit dry.

The Platonic Solids (32 min)	Key Curriculum Press

The first 17 minutes is for students and illustrates properties of regular polyhedrons, shows why only five Platonic solids exist, and presents the mathematical heritage of the solids and their duals. The next 15 minutes for teachers gives more background mathematics and explains ways in which to use the materials from the Visual Geometry Project.

Professor Devaney Explains the Fractal Geometry of the Mandelbrot Set (45 min)	Key Curriculum Press

Nowhere will you find a more cogent and understandable explanation and demonstration of what the Mandelbrot set is.

The Stella Octangula (25 min)	Key Curriculum Press

It's amazing how much mathematics can derive from studying a single shape. This video offers three computer-animated views of the intriguing stellated octahedron. The video's final 10 minutes is for teachers, providing more background mathematics and explaining ways in which to use the materials from the Visual Geometry Project.

The Story of Pi; The Theorem of Pythagoras, Similarity (25 min each)	NCTM, Dale Seymour Publications

Each of these excellent films is a stand-alone part of Cal Tech's Project Mathematics! series. Lively graphics and animations communicate the essential mathematics. Student workbooks that integrate classroom activities are available for each video.

Three-Dimensional Symmetry (17 min)	Key Curriculum Press

There are some things you just can't illustrate on a chalkboard. Transformations in three dimensions is one such topic. Accompanies materials of the same name from the Visual Geometry Project.

Sheldon G. Berman's All-Stars

These books are deserving of separate and top billing.

Outstanding Escher book

Locher, J. L., *M. C. Escher: His Life and Complete Graphic Work*

Outstanding visual impact in nature and science

Feininger, A., *The Anatomy of Nature*
Greco C. and S., *Piercing the Surface: X-Rays of Nature*
National Wildlife Federation, *Patterns in the Wild*
Neill, W., and Murphy, P., *By Nature's Design*

Outstanding visual impact in pattern and design

Beard, Colonel R. S., *Patterns in Space*
Grafton, C. B., *Optical Designs in Motion with Moiré Overlays*
Hargittai, I. and M., *Symmetry: A Unifying Concept*
Kim, S., *Inversions*
McKillip, R., *The Celtic Design Book*
Slocum, J., and Botermans, J., *Puzzles Old and New*
Stevens, P., *Handbook of Regular Patterns*
van Delft, P., and Botermans, J., *Creative Puzzles of the World*

Outstanding teacher's resource

Beard, Colonel R. S., *Patterns in Space*
Boles, M., and Newman, R., *The Golden Relationship—Book 1: Universal Patterns*
Boles, M., and Newman, R., *The Golden Relationship—Book 2: The Surface Plane*
El-Said, I., and Parman, A., *Geometric Concepts in Islamic Art*
Garland, T., *Fascinating Fibonaccis: Mystery and Magic in Numbers*
Grunbaum, B., and Shephard, G. C., *Tilings and Patterns, An Introduction*
McKim, R. H., *Thinking Visually*
Pearce, P. and S., *Polyhedra Primer*
Stevens, P., *Handbook of Regular Patterns*
Wells, D., *The Penguin Dictionary of Curious and Interesting Geometry*
Williams, R., *The Geometrical Foundation of Natural Structure*

Outstanding Activity Source

An asterisk (*) indicates a recommendation for construction projects.

*Bain, G., *Celtic Art: Methods of Construction*
Boles, M., and Newman, R., *The Golden Relationship—Book 1: Universal Patterns*
Botermans, J., *Paper Capers*
Fusè, T., *Unit Origami*
Grafton, C. B., *Optical Designs in Motion with Moiré Overlays*
Hiner, M., *Paper Engineering*
Laycock, M., *Bucky for Beginners—SYNERGETIC Geometry*
*Oliver, J., *Polysymmetrics*
Pentagram Design Limited, *Pentagames*
Pentagram Design Limited, *Puzzlegrams*
Pohl, V., *Enrich Geometry Using String Designs*
Schattschneider, D., and Walker, W., *M. C. Escher Kaleidocycles*
Serra, M., *Patty Paper Geometry*
*Seymour, D., *Geometric Design*

Catalog Sources

Most engaging teachers are forever foraging for new materials with which to entice and delight their students. In education nearly 90% of all teacher support materials and resources are purchased through catalog sales. I encourage you to get and peruse catalogs from the following organizations. Their product lines and target audiences are diverse, but all offer items that are excellent in the geometry classroom.

Creative Publications
1300 Villa Street
Mountain View, CA 94041
(800) 624-0822

Critical Thinking Press
P.O. Box 448
Pacific Grove, CA 93950-0448
(800) 458-4849

Cuisenaire Company
P.O. Box 5026
White Plains, NY 10602-5026
(800) 551-RODS

Dale Seymour Publications
P.O. Box 10888
Palo Alto, CA 94303-0879
(800) 872-1100

Design Science Toys
1362 Route 9
Tivoli, NY 12583
(800) 227-2316

Dover Publications
31 East Second Street
Mineola, NY 11501
(516) 294-7000

Educational Teaching Aids
199 Carpenter Avenue
Wheeling, IL 60090
(800) 445-5985

Geyer Instructional Aids
P.O. Box 10060
Fort Wayne, IN 46850
(800) 447-9368

Key Curriculum Press
P.O. Box 2304
Berkeley, CA 94702
(800) 995-MATH

Media Magic
P.O. Box 598
Nicasio, CA 94946
(800) 882-8284

Mindware
6142 Olsen Memorial Highway
Minneapolis, MN 55422
(800) 999-0398

Other publishers and companies

Activity Resources
P.O. Box 4875
Hayward, CA 94540
(510) 782-1300

Addison-Wesley
Attn: Order Services
1 Jacob Way
Reading, MA 01867
(800) 358-4566

Ballentine Books
Order Department
400 Hahn Road
Westminster, MD 21157
(800) 733-3000

Binary Arts Corporation
5601 Vine Street
Alexandria, VA 22310
(800) 468-1864

Birkhauser
Department Y886
333 Meadowlands Parkway
Secaucus, NJ 07094
(800) 777-4643

Buena Vista Home Video (Disney)
Attn: Consumer Relations
P.O. Box 908
Lakewood, CA 90714
(800) 723-4763

Chartwell Books
Book Sales
110 Enterprise Avenue
Secaucus, NJ 07094

Chronicle Books
275 Fifth Street
San Francisco, CA 94103
(800) 722-6657

Delta Education
P.O. Box 3000
Nashua, NH 03061
(800) 442-5444

EPM Publications
1003 Turkey Run Road
McClean, VA 22101
(800) 289-2339

Fireside Books
Attn: Customer Service
200 Old Tappan Road
Old Tappan, NJ 07675
(800) 223-2348

Genkosha
Iidabashi 4-1-5
Chiyoda-ku, Tokyo, Japan
03-3263-3511

Stemmer House
2627 Caves Road
Owings Mills, MD 21117
(410) 363-3690

Tarquin Publications
Caller Box A-10, Cathedral Station
New York, NY 10025

Thames and Hudson, Ltd
Distributor: W. W. Norton and
Company
(800) 233-4830

TOBI Toys
P.O. Box 781
Geyserville, CA 95441

Tucker-Jones House
P.O. Box 231
East Setauket, NY 11733
(516) 751-8960

University of Washington Press
P.O. Box 50096
Seattle, WA 98145
(800) 441-4115

Vestron Video
P.O. Box 4000
Stamford, CT 06907

W. H. Freeman and Company
41 Madison Avenue
New York, NY 10010
(800) 877-5351

Zometool
P.O. Box 7053
Boulder CO 80306
(303) 786-9888

Pythagorean Press
P.O. Box 5162
Bradford, MA 01835
(800) 344-4501

The Quilt Digest Press
955 Fourteenth Street
San Francisco, CA 94114

Random House, Inc
Order Department
400 Hahn Road
Westminster, MD 21157
(800) 733-3000

Safe-T Products
P.O. Box 692
La Grange, IL 60525
(800) 601-2861

Schocken Books
Order Department
400 Hahn Road
Westminster, MD 21157
(800) 733-3000

Shelter Publications, Inc.
P.O. Box 279
Bolinas, CA 94924
(415) 868-0280

Simon and Schuster
Attn: Customer Service
200 Old Tappan Road
Old Tappan, NJ 07675
(800) 223-2348

Springer-Verlag New York, Inc
175 Fifth Avenue
New York, NY 10010
(800) 777-4643

NASA Center for Aerospace
Information
Attn: Document Ordering
800 Elk Ridge Landing Road
Linthicum, MD 21090
(301) 621-0390

Nasco
P.O. Box 3837
Modesto, CA 95352
(800) 558-9595

NCTM
1906 Association Drive
Reston, VA 22091
(703) 620-9840

National Geographic Society
P.O. Box 98175
Washington, DC 20090
(800) 647-5463

National Wildlife Federation
1400 Sixteenth Street NW
Washington, DC 20036
(800) 477-5560

Oxford University Press
2001 Evans Road
Cary, NC 27513
(800) 445-9714

Penguin USA
120 Woodbine Street
Begenfield, NJ 07621
(800) 331-4624

Pomegranate Artbooks
P.O. Box 980
Corte Madera, CA 94925

HarperCollins Publishers
1000 Keystone Industry Park
Scranton, PA 18512
(800) 242-7737

Harry N. Abrams, Inc
100 Fifth Avenue
New York, NY 10011
(800) 345-1359

Henry Holt and Company, Inc
115 West Eighteenth Street
New York, NY 10011
(800) 488-5233

Houghton Mifflin Company
13400 Midway Road
Dallas, TX 75244
(800) 733-2828

HP Books
360 North La Cienega Boulevard
Los Angeles, CA 90048

John Wiley and Sons
1 Wiley Drive
Somerset, NJ 08875
(800) 594-5396

Little Brown and Company
Order Department
200 West Street
Waltham, MA 02154
(800) 759-0190

McGraw-Hill Company
P.O. Box 545
Blacklick, OH 43004
(800) 722-4726

MIT Press
55 Hayward Street
Cambridge, MA 02142
(800) 356-0343